"I can't marry without love,"

Brooke said very firmly. "I'm sorry, Mr. Corelli, but I intend to have a sizzling love affair, not a cold-blooded marriage—even if it is comfortable."

"That could happen to you, as well," Paul assured her dryly. "You're not unattractive."

Their eyes clung for a second and Brooke felt engulfed in a sense of total unreality. Paul Corelli could be dangerous. There was a sensual quality in him that could devastate a woman's emotions. She would be mad to even consider his proposal.

And then she remembered what it had felt like to be in his arms and a sudden hot excitement swept through her body....

Other titles by
MARGARET WAY
IN HARLEQUIN ROMANCES

Other titles by
MARGARET WAY
IN HARLEQUIN PRESENTS

Many of these titles are available at your local bookseller
or through the Harlequin Reader Service.

For a free catalogue listing all available Harlequin Romances,
send your name and address to:

HARLEQUIN READER SERVICE,
M.P.O. Box 707, Niagara Falls, N.Y. 14302
Canadian address: Stratford, Ontario, Canada N5A 6W2

or use coupon at back of book.

Wake the Sleeping Tiger

by

MARGARET WAY

Harlequin Books

TORONTO • LONDON • NEW YORK • AMSTERDAM
SYDNEY • HAMBURG • PARIS

Original hardcover edition published in 1978
by Mills & Boon Limited

ISBN 0-373-02258-1

Harlequin edition published May 1979

CHAPTER ONE

FROM long habit, Brooke closed her ears to her mother's voice, but Louise sat straight-backed and glassy-eyed, like some exquisite doll propped up on the sofa, while the light, petulant voice droned on through the almost daily litany.

'... not that either of you consider me! I'm just your mother. It's my duty to fret myself into a breakdown. A *breakdown*, nothing less! If only things were as they were!' This very bitterly, suggesting a terrible picture of present squalor instead of their beautiful, peaceful surroundings. 'Louise, you're the eldest, the beauty of the family. The least you could do is marry Patrick. He's a good Catholic and the family have pots of money!'

'Oh, Mother!' Louise broke into a wail.

'Why not Corelli?' Brooke suggested sardonically. 'In times of crisis, one might dare wake a sleeping tiger!'

'You're mad!' Louise said soberly. 'I wouldn't know how to handle him.'

'Maybe you'd better learn how!' Brooke's golden-green eyes studied her sister's petite, porcelain-look figure. 'He may not be the gentleman Mama wants for her precious lamb, but the prospect of getting our hands on all that loot would be beautiful. I wouldn't have to go out to work and we wouldn't have to sell Wintersweet. That's what it's all about, isn't it, Mamma?'

5

'I'd sell myself first!' Lillian Howell announced passionately.

'Oh, my!' Brooke choked back an involuntary laugh. 'Could anything be worse?'

'It will be a damned sight worse in every way if one of you doesn't marry money!' Lillian said, trembling. 'Why Poppa had to die and leave me in this dreadful predicament I'll never know. It's all been so very *wearing*. A widow with two daughters. Why didn't I have a son to build on inherited money? At least I gave you both a decent education and you've always had the prettiest clothes!'

'Lou has!' Brooke pointed out without rancour.

'That's news to me, miss. You're just jealous because you never got *my* looks. I tell you I'm sick and ashamed neither of you can make a brilliant match. All the efforts, the endless sacrifices, come to nothing!'

'You mustn't give up hope, Mamma!' Louise murmured sweetly.

'Isn't there a saying about storming Heaven?' Brooke asked with dry mockery. 'You two start praying. I'm fast moving towards middle age!'

'At twenty-four?' Louise said in bafflement. 'I'm two years older.'

'Aren't you lucky!' Brooke said lightly. 'You have the first chance at Corelli.'

'He can't possibly be interested in me!' Louise answered very modestly, for such a beautiful girl.

'Everyone says he is.'

'He'd be a fool if he wasn't!' Lillian broke in on her younger daughter, annoyed. 'It isn't likely he'll find anyone prettier or sweeter than my Louise!'

'*I'm* here, Mamma!' Brooke offered, knowing quite well the kind of answer she invited.

Her mother stared at her steadily, then she turned in her chair to feast her eyes on her favourite daughter. Louise was the apple of her eye, a faithful reproduction of herself at the same age—golden-haired, blue-eyed, heart-catchingly pretty. 'It's not normal to reach your age, Louise, and not be engaged.'

'But I must really be in *love*, Mamma!'

'What rubbish!' Lillian said shortly. 'That's all very fine in theory, but I know better. Your future husband simply has to have money. Love will come later, you'll see.'

'What if she has to wait for a long time?'

'At least she'll be kept in style!' Lillian answered her younger daughter sweepingly. 'In the old days, of course, Mr Corelli wouldn't have been on our list, but now it seems we have to consider him.' She looked down at her hands, comforted by the flash of the big solitaire diamond. 'I've nothing against Mr Corelli ...' Lillian paused for a few moments of intense maternal consideration. 'He may not be one of us, admittedly, but it *is* something after all to be a millionaire in one's early thirties. What a pity you're such a tomboy, Brooke. I'm surprised you're not still climbing trees, always getting dirty and scratched. Such a harum-scarum child, and you haven't changed a great deal.'

'You don't really look at her, Mother!' Louise said protestingly. 'Even Nigel has to admit Brooke has the sex appeal!'

'What rot!' Lillian answered shortly. 'What lady needs sex appeal?' A spasm of distaste marred her still pretty face. 'No one notices Brooke beside you. You're the one with the face of an angel!'

'Then I'd like a powerful heap of Brooke's spice!' Louise persisted. 'Just don't ask me to encourage Paul

Corelli—that's simply going too far. I've considered the matter, but I've got no great confidence in myself to handle him. He's dangerous, like all exciting men.'

'Lots of girls would like to take your place!' Brooke pointed out.

'I believe so.' A smile of satisfaction curved Louise's soft mouth.

Seeing it and the irresistible impression Louise gave of a cream-fed kitten Brooke burst into a hoot of laughter, a young joyous sound that gave her mother no pleasure.

Lillian reacted with visible anger. 'I wouldn't expect you to take anything seriously, Brooke, though it's true you do have some assets.'

'Could I hear them?' Brooke invited, clearly in one of her challenging moods.

'Actually my concern is with Louise!' Lillian said grandly. 'I'm not going to be sidetracked with you. Tell me, darling,' she asked Louise, 'did you invite Mr Corelli to our party?'

Unexpectedly the sweet-natured Louise sounded a little huffy. 'I did ring him, but he may be out of town on business.'

'That figures!' Brooke murmured. 'He's the damnedest man isn't he? Rags to riches and all that stuff. Some kind of financial wizard. Smooth too, in a very foreign way. He even speaks very nicely. Altogether a bright boy—*too* bright! Is it possible he has Mafia connections?'

'*No!*' Louise exclaimed loudly.

'You're just that teeny little bit attracted to him?' Lillian asked hopefully.

Louise gave a faint smile, looking like a cat again. 'He's a very striking-looking man. Not handsome exactly, but, oh well ... sexy, I suppose!'

'You suppose right!' Brooke proceeded to drain her coffee cup. 'And he plays a very special kind of game. Are you acquainted with how he makes his money?'

'Why, the construction company?' Louise opened her blue eyes wide. 'I believe he owns a chain of hotels as well.'

'Ah so!' Brooke put her joined hands together under her nose and gave another dry laugh. 'Well, the soulless pursuit of a dollar has now given way to the hellbent pursuit of a suitable bride. Would you care to hear what Cathy Benton thinks of him?'

'No, I wouldn't!' Louise shook her golden bell of hair back. 'He's only being kind to her squiring her around.'

'That's not what I heard.' Brooke rolled her eyes. 'She's even been on his yacht, and you know what that means! How does it go again? Once aboard the lugger and so forth!'

Lillian's flat-eyed gaze rested on her younger daughter with displeasure. 'You're not interested in him yourself, are you, miss?'

'I like your frankness, Mamma, but I don't see myself as a helpless victim!'

'What an extremely odd thing to say.'

'Oh, I don't know,' Brooke said quite seriously. 'One knows just by looking at him he'd give a woman hell!'

'He's always particularly pleasant to me,' Louise maintained.

'That's different!' Brooke laughed, and relaxed her taut, slender body. 'Let's take a look at the pluses. Despite the supposed grinding poverty of his past he's every inch the tycoon now!'

'He certainly is!' Louise agreed, quite feelingly for her. 'I sometimes think he's far more knowledgeable and sophisticated than all the Patricks in the world put together.'

'No argument there!' Brooke dismissed her sister's most persistent suitor very briskly. 'There's good blood in Corelli,' she said thoughtfully, 'probably a *Story!*'

'One could scarcely ask him for it,' Lillian said grimly.

'It would be stupid, yes,' Brooke agreed. 'To be as big a success as he is, one would have to be ruthless and unforgiving, a Borgia offering the poisoned cup to anyone who offended him. What he needs now at this stage of his career is a little class, a beauteous society butterfly to give him a son. As a working girl I don't qualify, but Lou's ideal. Add to that a great big white elephant like Wintersweet and its gracious living on the grand scale. That would appeal to him, plus the entrée to high society!'

'His money can get him that already,' Louise pointed out as if the fact didn't really please her.

'No!' Brooke's firm tone reassured her. 'He needs a symbol, a romantic symbol. That's you, little darling Lou, plus the house. You'll make a truly beautiful mistress and with some money at our disposal we could really spread ourselves. I'm sure he'd be kind to your mamma and your spinster sister. It would be like the old days when Granddad was alive. I really can't wait until you marry him.'

'Maybe it's not me he wants!' Louise almost wailed.

'It *is*, you, darling!' Lillian's genuinely besotted voice overrode Louise's lack of confidence. 'You can't help knowing you're a very beautiful girl!'

'Not with you telling her all the time,' Brooke agreed.

'Considering how I've lived in Lou's shadow it's a wonder I haven't a crippling inferiority complex.'

'You were always the clever one!' Louise pointed out a trifle smugly.

'What's that got to do with it?' Lillian demanded. 'Don't think for a second a man wants a clever woman. Especially not one with red hair and a sharp tongue!'

'Yes, sir! They don't come any more frightening!' Brooke seconded lightly. 'Tell us, Lou, what are you going to do with him once you've got him?'

'Don't make fun of me!' Louise cried out emotionally. 'Please, please, *please!*, Clutching a rounded bosom, she jumped to her feet, her big blue eyes swimming with tears, and dashed from the room as though shaken to her very foundations.

'Good grief!' Brooke murmured flatly.

'You've upset her!' Lillian's voice rose sharply to her darling's defence.

'So it seems! I didn't realise she was taking me so seriously.'

'You don't want her to get him, that's why. You're jealous of Louise—one doesn't need a psychiatrist to see that!'

It struck Brooke suddenly that she was for ever turning aside her mother's accusations. 'That's absurd,' she said gravely, 'even funny in its way. No, Mamma, I'm not jealous of Lou. I never have been, I never will be. I love her and I don't in the least envy her anything.'

'So you say!' Lillian bit off instantly. 'You're like your father. You behave just as badly as you feel inclined and you're always sarcastic at your sister's expense!'

'If you like, I can go and stay at a boarding house.'

Lillian's apple blossom skin flushed alarmingly. 'It

just so happens, miss, we need the extra money you bring in. You've had years of sacrifice lavished on you, now it's your turn to do something for your mother and sister.'

'What a pity Lou doesn't feel inclined to find a job,' Brooke said seriously.

'*I* don't mind!' Lillian began heatedly. 'And Louise doesn't mind. You're the one who really minds. As your sister pointed out, aren't you supposed to be the clever one?'

Brooke simply shrugged her shoulders. Any conversation she had with her mother gave her a headache. 'I'm not trying to upset you, Mamma, and I'm not making obscene suggestions. Lou could find something and we do need the money. I love Wintersweet too, but it's impossible to keep it going on a high school teacher's salary!'

'*High school teacher!*' Lillian very nearly hissed such a worthwhile profession. 'Louise will marry *brilliantly*, you'll see!'

'If she doesn't, we've had it!' Brooke concluded succinctly. 'Or life as you've known it!'

Lillian never even heard her, her blue eyes glowing. 'Yes, a brilliant marriage! This Corelli is supposed to have amassed a fortune.'

'And you don't care how?'

'Of course I don't!' Lillian came back to a bewildered reality. 'I mean, he's not a criminal and all that grisly business. All I care about is seeing my Louise happy and keeping Wintersweet in the family.'

'A tall order and desperate enough for Lou to even think of Signor Corelli. All that sophistication might cover a whole cupboard full of dark secrets.'

'Nonsense!' Lillian's fine-boned face was showing its

tension. 'Mr Corelli is a remarkable man, very remarkable indeed. If he's not of our world, one must move with the times. Wintersweet is being threatened—our heritage. The house stands, but if I have to sell off any more it'll be filled with a load of old rubbish. How Maggie Symons must rejoice in our ill fortune. From nowhere I've practically made her the best antique dealer in town!'

'We went looking for her, Mamma, remember? Maggie has qualities we need, discretion and an unquestioned reputation in the business. I value her as a friend. She lived her life among the rich and when the money ran out she turned her knowledge to good account. Don't let's start on Maggie. She's gone to great lengths to help us.'

'And herself!' Lillian sniffed delicately, strangely jealous of a woman who was making her own way successfully.

'That's the way it works. Maggie never says a word, that's the main thing. Some would make quite a story of all our sell-offs!'

Lillian shook her fair head painfully. 'It *had* to be. Do you think I don't feel like smashing all the fakes about the place?'

'*Good* fakes.' Brooke attempted to appease her mother.

'When I think of what's gone!' Lillian cried with a bitter sense of injustice. 'The most beautiful furniture in the house, the Louis Quinze suite, the Boulle commodes, the marquetry tables, the matching mirrors, Poppa's Oriental collection, or most of it. Such a nightmare! All this could have been avoided if your father had lived.'

'Perhaps.' Brooke felt a sickening sense of loss. She

had spent most of her life wondering how different life might have been with her father around, but he had been killed in a riding accident when she was barely four and Louise an adorable six-year-old. Before that they had lived with Grandfather Ashton, Mamma's father, at Wintersweet. There was more than enough room for everyone and Grandfather's health had not been good and he had to be watched. Despite that he had lived to rear them, selling what he had to and holding on to what he could to see them through when he was gone. That was four years ago, and everywhere Brooke's eyes touched there was some treasured object or art work missing. The house still stood, a chaste Georgian mansion, but there were many empty spaces inside and the Ashton family collections going back over many generations had long since been housed elsewhere. They weren't poor, far from it. They could never be poor while they had the house, but fixed assets didn't provide ready money. They were living on the sale of one of the bronzes now and it was surely paying for the party Saturday night. Mamma was really a gambler and she was trying to redeem all her losses at once.

'And you, Brooke,' belatedly her mother's voice came to her ears. 'You make no attempt to develop worthwhile friendships. You don't even seem to care about your future, let alone mine or your sister's!'

'What you're saying is, I'm in no great hurry to get married?'

There was exasperation in Lillian's face. She was well aware of her younger daughter's ability to tune out and she deeply resented it. 'I don't really care whether you get married or not just so long as you assist me to aim high for your sister. She's our salvation!'

'And you're going to sell her to the highest bidder?'

Lillian flushed angrily and her mouth opened in a little gasp. 'Try and remember who you're talking to, miss. I love Louise. Never forget I want the best for her. She's not like you. She needs cherishing.'

'You mean she's afraid of work,' Brooke pointed out gently. 'And you made her that way, Mamma. Everyone works these days. Some even like it.'

Lillian was standing now, staring at Brooke as though hypnotised. 'I was only married for a little while, but you bring Blair back to me every day.'

'You must have loved him, Mamma!' Brooke stood up too, several inches taller than her mother. 'He didn't have any money, not real money like Granddad, but they still speak of his brilliance as an architect and there are quite a few private and public buildings to prove it. It's my tragedy too that my father didn't live. Apparently I'm just like him, and the art classes I give bring in extra money. Father would have made Lou do something to justify her existence. Looking pretty simply isn't enough!'

'I think it *is*!' The colour had quite left Lillian's pale cheeks. 'I was brought up to believe a girl stayed home until she was married. Louise is a great help and comfort to me and I treasure her companionship. Might I remind you you're not our only source of income. There are still things in this house that could bring in more than you'd earn in years!'

'I know that, and once we sell them we'll never get them back. I'm sorry I spoke. I never meant to upset you. Forgive me.'

'I try to, Brooke, believe me. The trouble is your ego is constantly being bruised. You mightn't be able to rival your sister in looks, but you could concentrate more on your good points. I haven't forgotten you need a new dress for the party. If you'd come to me and ask nicely as Louise does—but you'd think taking money from your mother was taking charity.'

'That's not true, Mamma!' Brooke went to take her mother's hand, but Lillian pulled it away, mouth trembling and visibly upset. 'I just don't like to worry you and I can make my own way.'

'Just like Maggie Symons, I suppose? She's the recipient of all your confidences. You don't seem to have any trouble talking to her!'

'Our minds meet, yes!' Brooke agreed quietly. 'Maggie's a wonderful woman. I wish you wouldn't always attack her, then use her like you do.'

Lillian's darkened gilt brows drew together. 'It's not the first time that woman's caused discord in this house. She's tried to influence you from the beginning. I know Poppa liked her, but she's the kind of woman who's only attractive to men. Now if I don't go Louise and I will be late for that luncheon, the first really pleasant outing I've had this week!'

'Enjoy yourselves!' Brooke said a shade wryly.

'You should come too,' Lillian said predictably. 'You don't take the trouble to get to know the right people. Outside of Maggie Symons, that is!'

Brooke gave up without sighing and settled back into her chair again. 'What would you like for dinner?'

'Please not chicken again! I'd like a change.'

'I'll see what I can do!' Brooke murmured, her irritation and dismay subsiding into humour. 'The secret is in the budgeting. I guess you aren't interested in sandwiches?'

Lillian simply waved a hand and walked away. 'How insensitive you are!'

Am I really? Is that how I seem to you? Brooke continued to sit chin in hands, looking out over the terraced gardens that swept down to the blue, sparkling harbour. It was spring and the great banks of azaleas and rhododendrons had broken into beautiful drifts of flower, their fallen petals resting on the velvety lawn. A white latticework gazebo nestled amid the magnificent old shade trees that reached high into the radiant blue sky and from this angle of the calm sun porch no neighbouring building could be seen.

Wintersweet, a house of quiet splendour, or it had been in her grandfather's heyday. Pieces of sculpture had been removed from the garden and the fountain no longer played. Though she tried to make a joke about their less than heroic stand to save it, its decay was affecting her deeply. This was her home and she loved it perhaps more than her mother, and certainly more than Louise who frequently complained that such very large houses were hopelessly outdated. They were too, in their way, but they gave such a tremendous feeling of grace and beauty and *space*, no sacrifice seemed too much to keep them. They could sell Wintersweet tomorrow and do very well out of it, but first Louise had to be given her storybook chance. Life was one long romance and soon the handsome knight on a snowy white charger would come to claim Princess Louise for his own and while he was at it he would buy and refurbish their wonderful old castle.

Dreams, but were they possible? For an instant Brooke had a sharp mental picture of Paul Corelli the first time she had seen him. It was months ago when he had first appeared on the fringe of their particular group of friends; *old money*, as Lillian liked to call it, as opposed to the newly rich. Paul Corelli had appeared in the city out of nowhere, accumulating in a few years what seemed to be millions and a wealth of conflicting stories concerning his background. Some said he was an aristocrat all the way. Others maintained he had writhed and twisted and fought his way up from the gutters of Naples to become a ruthless, self-made millionaire.

Either way he had tremendous sardonic self-assurance and a certain sombre magnificence, until he smiled. Then the sex appeal spilled over and the brilliant eyes went velvety and one noticed what beautiful white teeth did for a darkly olive complexion. No one could possibly overlook him, certainly not a woman. Brooke shivered as if there was a cold breath of air on her back. Poor little Lou and Corelli? It was almost unthinkable, like mating a kitten with a tiger.

Again she saw in her mind's eye that ruthless dynamism married to her sister's enchanting, dreamy sweetness. Louise would be ruled into the ground even as she was supported in fine style. A man like Corelli could teach a woman how to suffer, Brooke was certain of it, and dislike stirred in her. She had had occasion to cross swords with Signor Corelli the few times they had found themselves in one another's company—a virtually instinctive and uncontrollable thing as though they were familiar to one another but natural antagonists. Brooke apparently looked and behaved exactly in the manner Signor Corelli least admired in a woman and he was almost at the point of telling her so. However, he would have to put up with her if he hoped to marry into a family of influence, and Brooke fancied he had an obsessiveness to do so.

The Ashton family might have fallen on hard times, but they had a relatively lustrous background going right back to the early days of the colony of New South Wales when Rupert Ashton had built Wintersweet along the lines of his old family home of Ashton Hall in Suffolk, England. Superb English and French furniture had come with him, silver and porcelain and an English gentleman's cultivated tastes. The Ashton men had gone off to two world wars and few of them had returned. Her uncles Jonathan and Hugh, her mother's brothers, had died in a New Guinea jungle when they were scarcely into their twenties. Now all that remained of the family was the three of them and Great Aunt Melville.

If Wintersweet was to be saved, none of them could do it on their own. It was first and always a rich man's home, a convincing status symbol to show the world. Louise would grace it beautifully, but she would need a team of servants to do all the work, and one hardly associated her with management.

An hour later Brooke was saying almost the same thing to Maggie. 'Hm, yes, I see what you mean.' Maggie tenderly shifted a delicate little figurine of a shepherdess, that could only be Meissen. 'Like Louise, don't you think?'

'Beside her I feel like Wonder Woman!'

Maggie turned around and slowly shook her dark head. 'It will take time to clear your vision. Perhaps only a man will do it for you. You can't begin to see yourself as you really are, only in contrast to your mother and sister.'

'Well, you must admit their looks are entrancing!'

'Hmm!' Maggie took time to answer. It was after closing time Saturday morning and all her clients and visitors had gone. 'I like yours a whole lot better and so do a lot of other people. Louise is a delightful child and that's all she'll ever be. You have the makings of a very splendid old lady, a matriarch with dozens of adoring grandchildren round your feet.'

'So I should think, that's if I ever get married.'

'You're no different from all the other girls,' said Maggie, and took a moment to put a pottery owl in her handbag, a gift from one of her irreverent friends and one they had placed behind the Meissen shepherdess. 'Really, honey, I'm sorry. You've got a lot on your mind, haven't you? I find it very odd myself that Mr Corelli should be interested in Louise. In you, yes. In Louise, no!'

Brooke's vivid face showed her surprise. 'You're being humorous, surely?'

'Not at all, dear!'

'Then that's extremely odd!' Brooke pondered briefly. 'I would say I antagonise him every time I open my mouth. He certainly gives that impression.'

'Of course!' said Maggie with womanly acceptance, 'that's a by-product of attraction.'

'Unlikely, Maggie. It's quite plain; he doesn't like me and as a matter of fact I don't care for him. It's a very serious matter thinking of letting him marry my sister.'

'Are you sure he wants to?' Maggie asked with a good degree of doubt.

'Between them, Mamma and Louise think they can swing it.'

'Then it should take a good deal of the pressure off you. I don't know why you don't say hell and damnation to both of them. I mean, just because you have red hair you don't have to play Cinderella.'

'Ah well!' Brooke said tolerantly. 'There's the party next week.'

'The bronze went a long way!' Maggie said dryly. 'I do hope you got your share. I tried extra hard for you and even I was surprised at the price I got!'

'Yes, thanks, Maggie,' Brooke said a little dejectedly, and the older woman stared at her, seeing with her artistic eye what she considered to be a beautiful girl. Not the pastel toned figurine figure of the sister, Louise, but a tall, graceful girl with wonderful bright colouring. It was wrong the way Lillian had convinced her younger daughter that only petite blondes were ravishing. Brooke's face was in the modern manner, with very distinctive slightly irregular features. Her hair was a true titian, her almond-shaped eyes a clear, glowing golden-green. Not a freckle marred her beautiful creamy skin and her short nose tiptilted over a wide, full-lipped mouth. It was a gay, courageous sort of face, even a passionate face with none of the perfect tranquillity Louise's delicate, chiselled features displayed.

'Why don't you get yourself a new dress for the party?' Maggie said abruptly.

'I might at that,' Brooke declared unexpectedly. 'You'll have to come with me and help pick it out. You're such a beautiful dresser!'

'I try!' Maggie said, and looked away, pleased. She wasn't and never had been a good-looking woman, but she had style and wit and confidence and pretty nearly everyone thought her very attractive. Behind her hard-won success story was tragedy, for Maggie had lost her husband and son in a car accident from which she had emerged with only minor injuries. Despite the fifteen years that separated her from that dreadful day she still experienced her moments of stifling despair, and she saw in Brooke the daughter she might have had, vital

and loving, swift to humour and compassion. 'I'll tell
you what,' she said impulsively, 'I have to fly down to
Melbourne on Tuesday. Some old dear has some
Chelsea cups and saucers she wants to show me—at
least she thinks they're Chelsea, and they have the gold
anchor marks and period. I'll call in on Martina Linden
personally and pick something out for you. Something,
just you. I know your size and I know how you could
look. Why should Louise get all the pretty dresses?
You have the ideal model figure!'

Brooke picked up a beautiful silver gilt table basket
and held it admiring the superbly pierced panels.
'Georgian?'

'Mid-Georgian. The pair of sauce-boats over there
came with it. An old lady on the North Shore, a sweet
old thing, we've become quite good friends. I often
pop in on her, but she has precious little left to sell!'

'All the old family silver disappearing!' Brooke
clicked her tongue sympathetically. 'I can't let you do
it, Maggie. You know perfectly well I can't afford
Linden prices.'

'Well, *I* can!' said Maggie, 'and I'm *going* to even
if I have to take it off you afterwards and wear it
myself. Of course I'll have to drop two stone, but if
you won't keep it?'

Brooke met Maggie's snapping brown eyes. 'I can
see I'll offend you if I won't!'

'The truth is, dear, you could look really beautiful
if you tried. Louise is a very sweet girl, but she's not the
beauty of the family in my opinion. Some find long-
stemmed redheads quite appealing and when they're
dressed by Martine Linden with Maggie Symons' help,
they're guaranteed to turn heads.'

'Well, it would be nice for a change!' Brooke gave a

wry smile, 'but the party is for Lou. She's our salvation, according to Mama!'

'Brooke, you know that's madness!'

Brooke greeted this with a shrug. 'Mamma and Lou are throwbacks to a more brilliant era, maybe Edwardian. Lou would be terrified of doing a day's work.'

'How extraordinary!' Maggie turned back from arranging her hair in a beautiful Adam pier-glass. 'Very few girls do nothing these days, and she's not stupid!'

'Not at all!' Brooke said loyally. 'It's just she can't begin to think of standing on her own two feet. Marriage seems the only way out. Mamma has drummed it into her. It's the only suitable career for a lady.'

'I notice she doesn't mind your working!' Maggie said crisply.

'Actually her first reaction was shock. You and I find pleasure and fulfilment out of a career. Mamma finds the idea vaguely contemptible and nothing will change her. In that way she hasn't moved with the times, but she has widened her vision to include Paul Corelli.'

'To get down to it she's playing the marriage game like the dowagers of old. Plenty of marriages of convenience happen, even today. Both of us know money tends to marry money, but it's a pretty brave thing to think of matching Lou with Mr Corelli. I mean, she's a very quiet girl and he's the most high-voltage man I've ever met. I mean, he's nearly as mettlesome as a racehorse. He even has a trick of throwing up his head. It's energising just to stand near him.'

'You sound as though you like him?' Brooke said in surprise.

'I'm not so old I can't be affected by a very sexy

man!' Maggie pointed out mildly, but there was a smile in her eyes.

'Dear!' Brooke drawled in a significant manner.

'Don't sound so surprised, I mean it. He's even come into the shop a few times.'

'Did he buy anything?'

'No, but he knew all the very best things. I have a feeling he will, *next* time. Actually, I can't wait. It's possible for me to admit at my age I find him fascinating.

'Why not?' Brooke said lightly. 'I suppose he is in a way. On the other hand, very little is known about him except he knows unerringly how to make money.'

'Well, surely you're not going to hold that against him?' Maggie asked rather ruefully. 'There's always got to be the start to a fortune. Look at most of the young men in your own circle. I won't say a few of them don't work hard even when there's no crushing need, but the money was made by those who went before them. Money does make money, dear, if it's invested wisely and a man has enough sons to take over control of businesses or holdings. Paul Corelli is a success story on his own. He's struggled and he's succeeded. It builds character.'

'Maybe it's not the sort of character I want for my sister!' Brooke frowned darkly.

'You're usually so generous, Brooke!' Maggie went to her magnificent Spanish ebony desk and locked all the drawers on one side. 'Something about Corelli makes you feel threatened.'

'Perhaps it's his arrogance,' said Brooke, busy covering her fingers with Victorian rings.

'Pardon me, darling, he's *not* arrogant. You're mistaking arrogance for the confidence of achievement. He can't help it if he has a superb head and he holds it up high. Italians are a very handsome race, don't you think?'

'I don't like him!' Brooke repeated perversely, then she held her left hand up for Maggie's inspection. 'Which one do you like?'

'Hard to say!' Maggie looked at the rings quite critically. 'On you I'd say the cabochon garnet in gold. You have good hands for showing off rings. That's an Italian piece, by the way—Castellani. He worked as a goldsmith and jeweller in London, early and mid-Victorian. I sold a beautiful lapis lazuli necklace of his the other day, excellent quality. Now what do you say to a bite of lunch?'

'Love to!' Brooke took the rings off her hand and replaced them in the display case. 'Mamma and Lou have gone over to the Watlings.'

'Why doesn't Louise marry Nigel?' Maggie suggested.

'Don't laugh, this is serious.' Brooke made a little grimace at herself in the pier mirror. 'Nigel couldn't help us hold on to the house, and that's what it's all about—Wintersweet. It was built for an Ashton and Mamma wants it to remain in the family.'

'Can't say I blame her!' Maggie gave an odd little smile. 'Few people could afford it these days and it would cost a fortune to build.' Maggie turned her head and the sheen of silver caught in her short dark hair. 'But it's a little cold-blooded, surely, to sell Louise to the highest bidder?'

'Mother loves her!' Brooke looked back at her friend with troubled eyes. 'The funny part is Lou would be prepared to go through with such a marriage, even with Corelli. There's a delicious little tingle of fear, but I really think she sees herself as just another precious object!'

'Yes, I don't know what Germaine Greer would think of her. Women's Lib really passed her by, and Lillian has never even heard of it. In fact, she has a positive genius for evading anything she doesn't want to know about. I've done my very best to help and the Ashton secrets are safe with me, but unless by a miracle one of you marries a very wealthy man Wintersweet has to go. It isn't possible to live in an empty house and frankly I don't want to see you lose any more. You could retain some of your beautiful pieces and move into a much smaller home. Others have done it. My mother did after Father died and death duties crippled us. I sympathise with your mother's feelings, but she's really so much better off than most people one can't lean too much her way. Everything is comparative. A lot of my friends would like to be as poor as your mother!'

'Yes,' Brooke said slowly. 'But I don't want to see her punished because she lives in a dream world. Granddad didn't prepare her for an ordinary way of life and Mamma has done nothing to prepare Louise. She's very beautiful and she's very charming, but I'm not at all sure Corelli wants her. All the money that's being spent on this party and he mightn't even come!'

'He'll come!' said Maggie, almost definitely. 'At least we can agree on one thing. He's a man who takes what he wants!'

CHAPTER TWO

BROOKE looked down at the exquisite burnished gold gown she was wearing. She had never worn anything remotely like it before and despite its remarkable flattery she was uncertain of the amount of bare back and creamy bosom she was displaying. Her jewellery was oriental, finds of Maggie's and gratefully borrowed; tasselled gold and jade pendants, with the lowest pendant of the necklace clinging to the cleft of her breast and the jade pendants of the eardrops swinging against her colour-blushed cheeks, intensifying the green of her eyes. She had taken Maggie's advice and used more make-up than usual, so that it seemed to her shocked and dazzled eyes that she had been transformed into a vaguely erotic beauty.

Clothes and make-up certainly made a difference, and she had never really noticed before that her body was perfect for draping clothes on. Nothing she had ever worn had suited her so well or made her look so flowerlike—an exotic, long-stemmed flower, it was true, but a flower all the same. Louise had always outclassed her in that department, but perhaps not tonight. Maggie had wonderful taste and she was wonderfully generous, but Brooke still felt a bit concerned about her new image. Nothing could possibly vulgarise such a beautiful dress, but she was completely unused to displaying her own beautiful body outside a swimsuit, and that seemed different somehow. That her body *was* beauti-

ful, she had never really seen before, accepting her tall,
willowy slenderness pretty much as she did her red
hair, a colour her mother particularly disliked despite the fact it ran in the Howell family. Tonight it
was a mass of bright copper curls, burnished like her
dress and haloing her vivid face like liquid fire. If it
wasn't beauty that looked back at her from the mirrored door of her dressing room, she didn't know what
it was. Perhaps Maggie was right after all and there
were different ways of being arresting.

There was a tap at her door and it opened and
closed gently. Brooke turned at once to smile at her
sister. 'You look beautiful!'

Louise didn't even answer, her eyes fixed on Brooke
as though she scarcely recognised her. Finally she
shook her golden head. 'Where on earth did you get
that?'

'An admirer!' said Brooke, making a game of it.

'I hope Mamma will let you wear it!'

'What's that supposed to mean?' Brooke felt a dull
sense of unease.

'We-ll!' Louise tilted her head to one side, her
Dresden blue eyes very wide. 'It's not by any means
the sort of thing you usually wear.' As she spoke she
moved around her sister, examining her from head to
toe. 'You're showing all your back and your chest.'

'So?' Better to keep up a maddening little show of
defiance than crumple, Brooke thought wryly.

'So it's not in the best of taste!'

'Rubbish! I've decided I've no reason to be ashamed
of my body, and I'm not showing all that much, after
all.'

'Don't say I didn't warn you,' Louise said placidly.
She came to stand beside her sister, staring at their

mirrored reflections. 'How different we are!' she said sweetly.

'You'll have to watch your weight later on,' Brooke felt driven into saying.

Louise's thin skin flushed pink. 'Patrick calls me a pocket Venus!'

'So you are! Sorry, darling, I didn't mean to be bitchy!'

'That's all right,' Louise said simply. 'When you're finished dressing Mamma wants to see you. I don't think she's going to like your dress or the way you've had your hair done. You look quite different!'

'Do you think so, really?' Brooke blew a kiss to herself. *Someone* had to.

'Yes, it's funny, but you do. I suppose red hair is bound to make you look colourful.'

'Perhaps I want something colourful to happen to me,' Brooke protested. 'Nobody sees me anyway beside you!'

A glimmering smile broke the seriousness of Louise's expression, though she didn't condescend to reply. In her blue chiffon dress she looked like a piece of gossamer, insubstantial as a dream and amazingly pretty. Not for the first time, Brooke thought it was no contest at all, but she stoutly determined she wasn't going to withdraw to her room and change her dress for the coffee-coloured silk chiffon her mother had suggested and actually picked out. It did nothing for her, though it was pretty and soft falling. Maggie had excellent judgment and Brooke reasoned that she had better believe in it.

Twenty minutes later, the first guests were arriving and there was no time for Brooke to change her dress, as her mother had requested with every appearance of shock. It was a little sickening to be hauled over the coals and told one looked artificial, but Brooke had walked away in the same instant and continued walking right down the staircase and back through the stair hall to the kitchen at the rear of the house. She had done all the liaison work with the caterers in any case. Let Louise be at her mother's side to greet the first guests; Brooke didn't want to cause any discordant notes.

The faces in the kitchen looked up alertly as she walked in and from their expressions it was fairly obvious that not everyone was going to share her mother's opinion. She relaxed and made a final inspection, admiring all the things she had admired before she had gone upstairs. Lillian had determined on a party to end all parties, and the most fashionable and expensive caterers had been hired. The whole works and be done with it! as Lillian had said. Brooke couldn't even bear to think of the cost. The flowers alone had cost hundreds of dollars and the tall, striking arrangements took care of the empty marble pedestals and gave a fresh, softening beauty to the large handsome rooms. All the main rooms, the two big reception rooms and the formal dining room appeared to be intact even though a good deal was missing, and besides, there were very few people familiar with everything that had belonged to the house in its heyday.

Brooke came suddenly out of her trance to see the head caterer, an attractive, very efficient-looking woman in her late fifties, smiling at her. 'Excuse me, Miss Howell, but may I say how stunning you look.'

'You may!' Brooke gave her a quick smile and moved to the door, the bright kitchen lights accentuating the lovely red-gold of her hair. 'I didn't intend to look quite so ...' she looked down at her dress and searched for a word.

'Why ever not?' The other woman raised her eyebrows disbelievingly. 'Stunning is the word. That dress is perfect on you!' She hadn't been inside the house an hour before she had become familiar with the terrain. Surely Mrs Lillian Howell would give anyone a terrible complex.

'Thank you!' Brooke said quietly. 'I can hear voices. I suppose we'd better start serving drinks.'

'Of course! *George?*' the woman turned around and spoke to a dark, rather handsome young man and he came forward with a smile already fixed on his face.

Brooke left them to it, resisting the cowardly notion to duck the party altogether. It was for Louise, after all, and she was really encircled by the kind of people her mother and Louise seemed to need to feel comfortable. People whose origins were well known and precisely what they were claimed to be: the established élite, except for Paul Corelli, and the possibility that he would turn up tonight was like bringing an alien from a larger world into their tight little circle. Looking as delighted as she could, Brooke walked out into the entrance hall to greet whoever might be about.

By nine-thirty, Corelli still hadn't arrived and Louise's soft radiance was beginning to flatten out like the bubbles in a glass of champagne. With big, blond Patrick constantly at her side she still kept looking towards the great cedar double doors as though Corelli was about to leap through them like the tiger Brooke often called him. Even Lillian kept turning her beautifully groomed head as though to mark the arrival of the night's 'star'. Corelli had an ability to generate excitement and his extraordinary success made it a whole lot easier for him to become one of them, but Corelli didn't arrive.

Brooke took his absence in her stride, determined not to become violently affected. The house was ideal for a big party and there were groups of people everywhere, laughing and chattering and keeping an eye on the drink waiters, exchanging all the gossip, their confident faces making it instantly known they were sophisticated, prosperous and very well informed. It was an open secret that Louise was going to be auctioned off to the highest bidder and they made much of it among themselves. The present owners of Wintersweet were living on borrowed time and a few discerning eyes detected the absence of one or other precious objet d'art.

Brooke, to her astonishment, found herself almost monopolised by Nigel Watling, one of Louise's long-standing admirers. He drew her out on to the terrace frequently to dance and Brooke had to admit she enjoyed it. The terrace looked magical by night, lit by a series of great tulip-shaped lamps and decorated with huge flowering pots of camellias and azaleas and cymbidium orchids. The chaste white pillars that supported the roof were almost covered by the foliage of the beautiful climbing redwing philodendron and the gardens beyond were illuminated by hidden lights in the trees.

'I'm not kidding!' Nigel breathed almost into Brooke's ear. He wasn't tall and their eyes were almost level. 'You look terrific tonight, just like a photo in a glossy magazine. You've been shopping and had your hair done.'

'I'm glad it wasn't all wasted!' Brooke smiled.

'Hell!' Nigel pulled her to him almost roughly. 'Why don't we just cut out of here?'

'Funny!' She stared at him. 'It's stuck in my head that you're Lou's friend.'

'I like it right here with you. I've said all along you've got the sex appeal. You light up in a way Lou never could. Incidentally, this party is an awful waste, isn't it? I don't suppose for one moment Corelli will show up.'

'So?' Brooke tried to speak blandly.

'So we all know what's in your mother's mind!' Nigel offered in a drawl.

Brooke felt herself stiffening and she pulled away from him. 'Now you listen to me, Nigel!'

'Hush, not now!' He looked over her shoulder and smiled at the couple attracted by Brooke's raised voice. 'I'm sorry, pet. No one can blame her for her strategy. It's just that I don't think he's all that interested in Lou. You can't blame him, she's a very pretty girl and she's thoroughly sweet and unspoiled considering, but she hasn't got a whole lot of character!'

'She's smart enough for you!' Brooke said heatedly.

'Gee, doll, I'm not in Corelli's league. Simmer down. I've noticed your hot temper before. Does it go with your blood?'

Brooke shrugged her creamy sloping shoulders, her voice curt with irritation. '*I* think Lou's too darned nice for the likes of Mr Corelli.'

'So do I,' Nigel said reasonably. 'But that's what this evening's gathering is all about. I mean, it's a wonderful party and the house looks great, a showplace, but is Corelli going to admire it sufficiently to want it?' The half mocking quality left Nigel's smooth, round face. 'You do get my point? It seems to me you make all the sacrifices in this family. Mother thinks it's a shame.'

'Big houses are always a lot of trouble!' said Brooke, sidestepping the issue.

'Then why don't you sell?'

Brooke gave a little sigh. 'It's almost unthinkable to associate Wintersweet with anyone else but our family.'

'Exactly!' Even Nigel sighed. 'There's no use Lou pinning any vague hopes on me. The old law firm is doing fine, but I could never rise to a forty-roomed mansion. They don't build houses like this any more, and who wants them anyway?'

'I have to say I do!' Brooke's golden-green eyes were touched with melancholy. 'Or at least I'd like to see it remain in the family.' Nigel was holding her too closely and she became aware of it. 'Surely you're not thinking of switching your affections to me?' she asked dryly, and eased her slender body away.

'I've always been aware of you, Brooke,' he said seriously, 'but you couldn't seem to notice. Lou is much easier to pay compliments to. She loves them and she listens. You've always got something else on your mind.'

'Why, Nigel!' she exclaimed, almost bewildered.

'It would take only a few minutes to convince you.' He was talking softly, close to her ear, imposing his feelings upon her, and Brooke had the decided impulse to draw back. Previously she had almost ignored Nigel, thinking him her sister's friend, but now it was obvious his interest was in her. He put out a hand to caress her cheek and she flung her head back almost wildly.

'*No!*'

'You know, you're really wild!' There was excitement in his voice and surprising strength in his hands.

'Let's go inside,' she said swiftly, aware he was trying to guide her into a shadowy corner.

'Don't you trust me?'

'No.' She looked him directly in the eye and he smiled.

'But I'm only good old Nigel, remember? Not the big-cat man, Corelli. Haven't you noticed the way he moves, all that dark sinuous grace? Now he really turns you on, doesn't he?'

Brooke jerked to a halt in honest astonishment. 'I don't think I'm hearing right!'

Nigel lifted his hands and held them in the air as though desparing of her answer. 'Doesn't he?' His slate-coloured eyes looked suddenly hard.

She was startled and looked it, ready to fly into an inexplicable rage. 'I've never heard anything so ridiculous in my life. What little I've seen of Signor Corelli I dislike intensely!'

In the passion of her denial, she failed to notice Nigel's vaguely convulsive expression. His eyes went beyond her, a faint flush coming to his cheeks.

Brooke swung about imperiously, her lovely long skirt fluid about her slender body. Paul Corelli stood almost directly behind her, his expression one of sharp amusement though the flame of the lamplight was reflected in his black, heavy-lidded eyes.

'Please do go on!' he invited, in his compelling, attractively accented voice. 'Such a respected opinion!'

Louise was there beside him, her delicate little face almost frostbound. 'Oh, Brooke, how could you?'

Brooke's heart was racing, but she gave Corelli her hand after an instant and he raised it to his mouth, without actually touching it. 'I'm sure Mr Corelli is thick-skinned enough to take it!' she said sweetly.

'Insensitive to insults, *signorina*!'

There was a toughness and arrogance about him that would always make him stand out. With anyone else

Brooke would have been on fire with embarrassment, but with Corelli she felt an upsurge of defiance, a mutual veiled hostility that made her long to put him in his place. It was quite true he moved with the grace of a big cat of the jungle and with almost as much menace.

Louise's pretty colour had faded and she looked as if she was about to faint. 'I suggest you apologise to Paul!' she said urgently to her sister. 'Mamma won't be pleased.'

'I can't possibly do it!' Brooke protested with an unconscious look of challenge and defiance that Paul Corelli neatly caught. 'Mr Corelli can't have his own way in everything.'

'I mean to,' he said, apparently idly, and Louise's expression changed into one of painful longing.

'I'm glad you're so tolerant, Paul. Sometimes Brooke is the absolute limit!'

'I have to admit it was wonderful when little girls were seen and not heard!' he murmured suavely, his dark eyes slipping over Brooke's face and slender body with a kind of authority.

Brooke knew a moment of measureless anger. How dare he look at her like that? As if he knew every last little thing about her. 'If you're going to dance, don't let us stop you,' she snapped.

Corelli's black eyes registered sardonic amusement. 'You do me a great honour!'

Before she could stop him or even know what he was about he pulled her towards him with a deceptive gentleness that she was sure could turn into ferocity. 'Don't look so tragic, *piccola*!' he said to the startled Louise. 'Your sister doesn't really upset me. I believe redheads are known to have runaway tongues!'

'May I?' Nigel flickered a brief, telling glance at Louise and when she showed not a spark of reaction he caught her hand. 'Dance with me Lou. *Now!*'

She went into his arms like a sleepwalker, both of them staring after Brooke and Corelli, while Brooke with so many glances upon her felt well and truly on her mettle. 'Does a chance overheard remark entitle you to hurt me?' she asked sweetly.

He looked down at her, on his dark face a curious mixture of hauteur and amusement. 'Let me tell you, *signorina*, there's nothing I'd like better, but I'm not hurting you at all!'

She lifted her titian head, forcing herself to smile. The very air around them was crackling with tension but deliciously perfumed. 'We're very glad you could make it tonight.'

'You don't really expect me to answer that, do you?' He was leading her easily, a superb natural rhythm in his hard graceful body. 'Relax!' he said, and made a sound of faint exasperation. 'That's better! A woman should naturally yield.'

'I appreciate that you might think so!' Her green eyes flashed at him and he laughed beneath his breath, as dark and menacing as a fiend incarnate.

'It's a pleasure to see you in character, *signorina*, I've always known what kind of female you really are!'

'Really, I don't understand you!' She was colouring and very nearly stammering, absurdly aware of his curiously sensuous effect on her and cursing herself for it.

'No?' He lifted his fine black brows superciliously. 'Tonight you look like a woman to threaten any man's peace of mind.'

'Surely not!' she burst out rashly. 'I've never been blind to *your* attitude!'

'Tell me!' he invited with a look of amused insolence.

'I don't believe I have to. These things are usually mutual.'

'What things?'

'Oh, never mind!' she said shortly, and made the mistake of staring up into his face. On all other occasions she had glanced at him only fleetingly, now she was made aware of the deadly attraction that drew most women like a magnet. He wasn't conventionally handsome, but he was certainly very striking. His features were all Italian: the splendid dark head with its thick deep waves, the broad brow, the fine, dark olive skin, the large brilliant dark eyes, the once aquiline nose that had been broken at some stage of his life, the wide sensuous mouth, the square deeply cleft chin. His grace of movement was Italian too and the dark resonance of his exceedingly attractive voice.

'That, I would say, is the first time you've ever really looked at me.'

There was a decided curl of sarcasm in his dark voice and Brooke pushed back against his hard controlling hand. 'Strangely, yes. The thought has always impressed itself on my mind that you're my sister's friend.'

'I imagine you thought the same thing of Watling,' he answered suavely, watching a storm of feeling flash into her almond-shaped eyes.

'Nigel *is* Louise's friend!'

'He looked remarkably as if he wished to be your lover.'

'It would take a miracle, Signor Corelli.'

'Good, then I will not have to kill him.'

She waited until the blood had stopped pounding in her ears, but by that time he had taken her hand and led her down the short flight of marble stairs into the surrounding garden. She couldn't look at him and she could make nothing of his strange taunt.

'Such a pity the statuary has been removed,' he commented briefly. 'The garden is beautiful, but it's being neglected. Everything is growing at will like a miniature rain forest. I like a little hint of informality, but there must be order underlying it.'

'You don't have to convince me,' she said a little bitterly. 'The grounds are very large and inexpensive gardeners are hard to come by these days.'

'Of course you are right!'

She couldn't see the irony in his eyes but she could hear it in his voice. 'It's no secret the Ashton fortune is dissipating rapidly,' she said.

'And you mind very much? I seem to have upset you.'

'It would amuse you, surely?'

He shook his dark head. 'Why do you think me so cruel?'

She stiffened and continued walking, feeling the cooling breeze on her face. 'It took a long time and a lot of money to build Wintersweet. You can't blame us for not wanting to see its ruin.'

'You agree then that your mother should sell her daughter?'

Taken by surprise, she was unprepared for the force of her anger. Her hand flew up of its own accord even as she watched it with a sort of horror. But it never connected. He caught it in mid-air and pinned her wrist, bearing her hand down again and holding it forcefully to her side.

'Be calm!' he said, almost gently, deriving some kind of sadistic amusement from her frail strength.

'And be careful what you say to me!'

'Surely in such a situation you must expect some scandalous comments?'

'Why did you come here?' she asked sharply, worried because her heart seemed to be hammering painfully. His hard grip hadn't lessened and she was making no effort to resist him.

He turned her to him and still she made no resistance. 'Because I wanted to talk to you.'

'No.' The imperious shake of her head rejected his explanation.

'I have been determined on it for a long time.'

'If it's something to do with Louise, you'll have to speak to my mother.'

'Louise is very pretty, but she's not right for my plans.'

'Whatever they are, I don't intend to listen.'

'Not even if something terrible might happen to you?'

'This is my own home and we're surrounded by people!' Brooke pointed out a little uneasily. They were, she supposed, almost invisible from the house and she was certain he was no gentleman. There was a distinctive flavour of purpose about him, a glorious ruthlessness that would ensure that he always got his own way. She told herself she wasn't going to be intimidated, but her agitation was fairly recognisable.

'Permit?' he said, and led her towards the marble garden seat. 'It won't be comfortable, but it's more pleasant to discuss business sitting down.' He glanced at her sidelong, speaking to her almost as if she were a child. 'There, that's better now.' Very politely he took his place beside her, his every movement so sure-footed and unconcerned he was making her feel even more confused and jittery.

'What is it you want to speak to me about?' she asked rather breathlessly. His arm was resting along the back of the bench and it seemed like a small crisis.

'You're afraid of me?'

'I am *not*!' Even she was aware it sounded like a hysterical snap.

He only continued to look at her while the breeze blew around them and the trees rustled and whispered in the night-time jungle. 'It is no secret at all that quite a few people expect me to marry your charming sister.'

'No secret at all!' she agreed dryly.

'And may I ask if you think so too?'

She answered promptly, throwing up her bright head. 'Unlike a lot of people, I'm not one of your admirers, Signor Corelli!'

'No matter, it's not necessary. Maybe you will believe *you* try my patience?'

'I think I've said before, these things are mutual.'

'I understand, I believe, but I feel I have better manners.'

'What a pity my Italian is so rusty!' The slow melodic cadence of his speech was really getting to her.

'You need a tutor. You should ask me.'

'I do know *andiamo, amico*!'

He gave a low, throaty laugh. 'I think you mean *addio*!'

'So I did!' She came to her feet with swift grace, but he put out his hand and drew her down again with peculiar light strength, a controlled power that made her more than ever aware of the intense force behind it.

'Let's get on with it, shall we? I am prepared to discuss the only thing of real interest to you, your home.'

'What on earth for?' she burst out with real impatience.

'If you'll be quiet I will tell you more about it. Forgive me, I see you're not used to holding your tongue.'

'It's normal and healthy to ask questions.'

'Not all the time!' he said dryly. 'Both of us are aware that your mother is prepared to gamble everything on marrying one of her daughters off to a man rich enough to appreciate all this.'

'You don't sound terribly disgusted?' she said waspishly.

'Come now, *signorina*, you know I'm Italian. Marriage is considered a very serious business and one must do well by the family. It is expected.'

'*Benissimo!*' Brooke drawled, slipping ironically into his language.

'Amuse yourself as you wish, *cara*, I know a way to cure it. I may have given the impression that I was in pursuit of your very pretty sister, but it is *your* hand I ask for in marriage!'

'I feel faint!' Brooke whispered, in a panic.

'You do not!' Very firmly he clasped his hand around her nape and pushed her head down. 'You breathe—breathe—and the moment will pass!'

It was extraordinary, but the touch of his hand seemed to quieten her jumping nerves. She began to inhale deeply and after a moment his hand fell away. 'This is no romantic proposal, *signorina*, but a contract, and I promise you it won't be unpleasant.'

'Mr Corelli—wait a moment, please!'

'I'm listening!' he shrugged.

'It may be like this in Italy,' she said helplessly, 'but we're much more progressive!'

'You mean you have a greater rate of divorce? Contrary to popular opinion, we are not a sentimental people. Money is always a consideration, it is much better to marry where it is than where it isn't. You too have a duty to your family. Your mother and sister are very charming but very helpless. One wouldn't like to see them struggling. Such a desolate vision! Louise has not been reared to be useful. She's like a pretty medallion one wears around the neck, a possession!'

The truth of that was hard to ignore and for a moment Brooke couldn't say anything. The innuendo was that *she* might prove useful, and she was anything but flattered.

'And how am *I* different?' His expression was impossible to read, but she could see the gleam of his eyes. They mightn't be amber, but he obviously could see in the dark.

'For one thing you have more spirit, more animation, very possibly, a brain.'

'Oh, thank you!' she said dryly. 'I assure you Lou has one too.'

'Undoubtedly, but I haven't seen a great deal of it so far. I appreciate your loyalty, but my mind is made up.'

He sounded so much a man whose every whim was obeyed, Brooke jumped to her feet, her hands fluttering in a storm of jumbled emotions. 'Oh, stop it, *stop it*! I can't possibly take you seriously.'

'Why not?' he asked, unperturbed by her performance.

The jade earrings were swinging against her cheeks and she stopped moving abruptly. 'It may be a solution so far as Louise is concerned, but in this case, Signor Corelli, I can work for a living.'

'So you can!' he said gently. 'And who is going to

wake up your dreamy little rabbit of a sister?'

'Obviously not you!'

He spread his hands in a foreign gesture. 'Let that be a lesson to you, *cara*, not to be too confident. Your mamma is already looking on me as a son-in-law.'

'And she'd be prostrate with shock if she knew you were talking this way to me. Even poor little Louise, it would be too much for her. Why on earth did you encourage her?'

'Questions, questions!' he chided with a faint sharpness in his velvety voice. 'You may be surprised to learn that I gave your sister very little encouragement. She is like a kitten, begging to be cuddled!'

'You're impossible!' said Brooke, keeping her voice down with an effort. 'It's on account of you Mamma, put on this dreadful party!'

He looked up at her with his luminous eyes. 'It's a heavy load of love you carry, isn't it, *poverina*?'

'I'm sorry, I don't know what that means?'

'You hurt. *Poor little thing.* You hurt yourself, you hurt your mother and your sister. Marry me and everything will come right.'

Her eyes closed and she seemed to sway. 'Louise may say yes to such a blessed event, Mr Corelli, but my answer is *no*!'

'Sorry, but I don't take no for an answer.' He was on his feet beside her, letting his hands fall with their full hard weight on her delicate shoulders. 'I am sure you are going to think about it. I am sure you are going to weigh up all the advantages. As part of our agreement I will restore Wintersweet to full dignity. I already know which treasures are missing and exactly where they are. I cannot promise to take within my home your mother and sister, but I will make it possible for them to

live in considerable style. Louise will no longer have to
go through a hell of recriminations if another millionaire doesn't show up. You see, *cara*, I know your beautiful mamma spits venom on occasions. I don't want any
of it in my eyes and I shall be very quick to protect my
wife!'

'You really are a tiger man!' she said beneath her
breath. 'I can't believe you've been stalking *me* all
this time.'

'It was not necessary to frighten you too early. You're
trembling like a leaf. On my account?'

'Not at all!' She tried to stand calm beneath his
hands. 'You're not suggesting you've fallen in love with
me?'

'*Dio*, no! I am not a fool, *signorina*, this love is too
much. I want a woman who will grace my home,
a woman who will promise, in time, to have my child.
I do not intend to be the last of my line.'

'Which is *what*?' Brooke asked with a desire to hurt
and humiliate him.

Hard fingers bit into the silken skin of her collar-
bones. 'You have had too much, *signorina*, almost
spoiled and crippled by being too rich, too young. You
may assume I know exactly who I am, and I am none
the worse for the lonely poverty of my childhood.'

'I'm sorry!' Despite herself she shuddered and
apologised. 'I didn't mean to be so rude, but it's partly
your fault. My mother might wish one of us to marry
money and because of it save Wintersweet, but surely
you understand I can't marry without love? No love
whatever!'

'I think you will!' he said abruptly. 'From the way
you are trembling I know you are far from indifferent
to me. Yes, it's unbearable, I know, for you to admit

it, so you may remain silent staring up at me with those great golden-green eyes. You are waiting for something to happen to you, aren't you? What do you want from life?'

'Not *you*!' she said fiercely.

'Let me finish. I have not the slightest doubt I could make you fall in love with me if I wished. I could even make you purr like your sister.'

'You couldn't!' Brooke very nearly shouted, almost ready to explode.

'I wonder——' he said. 'Anyway, it doesn't matter. You are a stubborn little creature, that is all. Much younger than your what—twenty-two?' He lifted her chin and looked into her pearly, illuminated face. 'We will try this marriage. You will have your lovely old house back again as that is what you want, and your mother and sister will be free to travel all over the world. I believe neither of them, for all their love of Wintersweet, wish to stay at home.'

'Oh, help me—oh, my God, I can't stand it!' Brooke threw her head up towards the stardusted sky.

'You are being ridiculous!' His face grew harder, taking on its cast of sombre magnificence. 'Is it so terribly frightening, the thought of being married to me?'

'You simply don't know!' she said mercilessly. 'I think you must be a little peculiar, Mr Corelli!'

'Paul!' he suggested firmly. 'You don't know the difficulty I have getting around your own name. It does not fall softly on the ear or the tongue. Isn't there some other name you have? Something more beautiful?'

'I'm sorry,' she said hotly, 'but as we're not going to get married it doesn't really matter.' Uninvited sensations were making her feel trapped yet aggressive. We must go back to the party. I'm sure our absence has been noticed.'

'Very much so,' he agreed dryly. 'Give me your answer and it will be all over the papers as well.'

'I'm sorry, Mr Corelli,' she said very firmly. 'It's my intention to have a sizzling love affair, not a cold-blooded if comfortable marriage.'

'That could happen to you as well. You're not *un*-attractive.' His fingers loosened their grip on her bare skin and it took moments for the heat of contact to wear away. Their glances clung for a second, Brooke's startled and outraged, Corelli's coolly disciplined as though what he was suggesting was simplicity itself.

Brooke had an engulfing sense of complete unreality. No wonder he had become so notorious, so rich; he had a frightening momentum about him that carried people and events along. She was so nervous she was lightheaded, and all the time he was observing her with intense, almost disinterested curiosity. He was speaking to her again, but she couldn't seem to concentrate.

'. . . it will be to your advantage. Each of us has something the other wants. You are only nervous, after all, and the sense of fright will pass away. Marriage will keep your old family home in the family and one day it will belong to your son.'

'Not by you!' she said faintly.

'But of course! Your feelings will change and I give you my solemn word I will not force you. After all, there is no need for you to produce my heir for a year or two.'

'You'll have to stop!' she said abruptly, 'I have the strangest ringing in my ears. It's dreadful really, like

a mounting headache. I know it might help in lots of
ways, but God knows, this is crazy! It's not even a
marriage in name only.'

'Would you find that less disturbing?' he asked
dryly.

'Of course, as I'm being bought!'

'My offer is not insulting, *signorina*,' he said softly,
'and you would be foolish to refuse me. Quite apart
from your temper and your unfortunate habit of speaking your mind you've made a favourable impression on
me. I don't mind in the least if you marry me for my
money, but I am a man who takes what he wants. In
time, when you are ready, you will be my wife as well
as my charming hostess. After all, I am under no illu-
sions about you. You are a passionate woman, or you
will be when you are taught to love.'

'Are you sure you would know how?' she asked
tightly.

'You can't be serious?' he bent his brilliant level gaze
on her. 'Would you like me to begin now?'

'I think you capable of anything!' she said dizzily,
and drew swiftly away from him. 'My answer is no,
Mr Corelli, and I won't change. You'd do better to
buy Lou. She has a far more tractable nature.'

His low laugh suggested he was amused by her passion. 'Think about it, little one. I would so hate to lose
you.'

'Please let's go back!' she said urgently.

'I don't think either your mother or your sister will
approve your decision.'

'Once they get over the shock!' she said shortly. 'My
mother's plans have been all for Louise.'

'I regret that Louise does not interest me in that
way!' he said suavely. 'I am searching for a bride—no

more, no less. I have no desire to tangle myself in the madness of love, but I would be a liar if I said you do not attract me as a woman. Dressed as you are at this moment, as you should be, you quite eclipse your sister, as a red rose eclipses a white camellia. There is much passion in you, much capacity for feeling. I must tell you now there is something else I would require you to do.'

Brooke's heart was beating unmercifully, but she turned her gleaming head. 'Anything else would be anti-climax, I'm sure!'

'Perhaps!' He stared directly down into her eyes. 'I have a daughter I would expect you to introduce to society.'

'A daughter?' For a moment Brooke was transfixed. 'Then you've been married before?'

'I didn't say that.' The striking dark face looked impossibly haughty, the black eyes beneath the strongly arching brows brilliantly cold. 'My daughter is a result of my liaison with a young girl I knew in another lifetime. She lives with my married sister in Kenya, but as soon as we marry, naturally I will want her with me. She has endured much being away from me for so long, but it was necessary for me to establish myself. Now I have the chance of marrying an authentic society beauty, Lucia will come to me. You can do much for her.'

'Yes, I see.' Brooke began to visualise herself as a nursemaid. 'How old is the child?'

'Sixteen,' he said, pinning her gaze.

'Good God!' Swiftly she let her eyes travel over his arrogant dark face, the perfection and elegant cut of his clothes. 'I can't believe it. You must have been a boy.'

'I was young,' he corrected. 'Neither was it my first affair, I'm afraid.'

Brooke took a deep even breath, pretending she was taking his words in her stride. 'No wonder you accept the question of marriage as a matter of course. No doubt you wouldn't consider the vow of fidelity?'

'I might,' he said lightly, then smiled at her burning expression. 'There are some women for whom a man would sacrifice anything.'

'And where is that woman? Have you met her?'

'I wish to God I had, but possibly such a woman doesn't exist.'

'Then I suggest you wait a little bit longer. I'm sure you could improve a great deal on me.'

'On the contrary, I'm not satisfied with postcards from my daughter. I want her here under my eye. I want her to be given every advantage.'

'I suppose you're aware I'm hardly of an age to make a good stepmother,' Brooke managed scathingly.

'But you can give me the promise of a son. I haven't worked so hard all these years for nothing. Now at thirty-five I want a settled home and a family. Respectability, *signorina*. It haunts me.'

'As well it might!' She regarded him with some spirit. 'I appreciate your position, Mr Corelli, but don't ask me to share it. I intend to take my time deciding whether I want to get married or not.'

'Look around you,' he invited. 'Your home will fall into ruin unless a rich man buys it, and very soon. There won't be all that many generous offers. Perhaps some real estate developer will pull it down simply to build an apartment block on it. Life would never be the same again for your mother even if your sister manages to marry some correct young man.'

'Which she will,' Brooke said in a cold fury.

'I doubt if her future husband would take in your mother.'

'Well, you're planning to evict her, aren't you?' She flung up her head, bewildered by his manner and his mockery, his complete lack of deference.

'I told you exactly what I intend to do. It would pay you to listen for once. Your mother would be free to lead the good life wherever she liked, free to visit her old home occasionally. She is in her element where the champagne is flowing. You will be free to choose the time you wish to live with me as my wife.'

'Which is never!'

'It is time we went back to the house,' he said, dismissing her heated response. He took her arm, guiding her as though she were a rag doll or already his chattel, and Brooke felt an uprush of feeling not unlike terror. He evidently excelled at getting his own way and there was a sensual quality in him that was devastating at first hand. Her thin, high heels dug into the lush grass and the music from the big, romantic white house spilled out into the night air and over them. She remembered what it was like to be in his arms and his plan for her future gave rise to a sudden hot excitement that swept through her body like wildfire. Paul Corelli was no man to become emotionally involved with. Hadn't she said all along that he would know how to make a woman suffer? His blood was too fiery even if his head was coldly and brilliantly calculating, and now this astounding news that he had a daughter. She was certain Louise had no knowledge of this, nor anyone else for that matter. He was the complete adventurer and in the grand tradition he was trying to sweep her off her feet.

Back up on the terrace Lillian appeared, apparently casually, starting forward with hostessy exclamations to grasp Corelli's arm and draw him back inside. As ever Brooke let her mother's light, brittle voice flow over her. She knew perfectly well that Lillian was almost livid with disappointment because she had apparently tried to monopolise Corelli's attentions. Probably she was only waiting her moment to tell her and Brooke would have to impart the whole incredible story. Corelli was trying to buy her, not Louise. Lillian would have great difficulty in accepting it, and who could blame her? She could scarcely realise his cynical proposal herself.

Across the beautiful, glowing room Brooke caught sight of her sister's face. By this time Paul Corelli had joined her and she was looking up at him with almost frightened fascination. Not in her wildest dreams would she have imagined that he had just proposed to Brooke. Everything bloomed for Louise—the parties, the flowers, the pretty dresses. Their mother had always seen to it. Now for the first time in all their long years together the prize bouquet was being offered to Brooke and instead of accepting it shyly she wished only to fling it back into Paul Corelli's dark, flamboyant face. She might feel weak with astonishment, even breathing with difficulty, but she would take good care she was never left alone with him again. Some men loomed larger than life size, and he was one of them.

Someone came close to her and grasped her arm. 'Heaven preserve you from your mother, darling!' Nigel said with some maliciousness in her ear. 'Choose any escort you please, but not Corelli.'

'Perhaps he chose me!' she murmured, unaware her eyes were sparkling like gems.

'Yes, indeed! I've always said your mother and sister seriously underestimate you. Will you look at poor old Lou now? Someone ought to go over and wake her out of her trance. Pretty as she is she looks almost foolish staring up at him like that. Tell me, pet, what did you talk about?' Nigel's eyes were sharp in his smooth, tanned face.

'Oh, this and that.' Brooke shook her head impatiently. 'I don't want to hear another word about Corelli. I've endured enough!'

'He isn't worth it!' said Nigel, and suddenly became very sure of himself. 'Isn't it about time supper was served? I'm getting hungry!' He slipped one arm around Brooke's narrow waist, thinking she bore not the least resemblance to her sister. The drink waiter came towards them and Nigel helped himself to two glasses of champagne, never understanding why Brooke tossed hers off so quickly. He had never seen her do such a thing before. Apparently she had changed in more ways than one.

CHAPTER THREE

'BROOKE!' Lillian swept into her bedroom, just as she was about to climb into bed. Behind her, Louise padded in her bare feet, her small face innocent of make-up and tear-stained.

'It's practically three o'clock in the morning!' Brooke protested, aware that Lillian was quivering with rage.

'Mamma——' Louise began uncertainly.

'Leave this to me, Louise!' Lillian said shortly. 'Nothing in the world would stop me now!'

'Have you come in to tell me I've damaged my reputation?' Brooke asked wryly.

Unexpectedly Louise began to cry and Lillian turned to her with great affection, pressing her into an armchair without a word. One hand came up and she stroked Louise's pretty blonde hair from her face.

'Don't be angry with me, Mamma!'

'I can't be angry with you, my darling!'

'Listen,' Brooke said from the bed, 'I'm bored and tired, what is it you want to say that's making Lou so unhappy?'

Lillian turned brusquely back to her younger daughter. 'What an impression you made tonight, miss! That *dress*—you're very extravagant with my money— the contempt you've shown for my plans!'

'Come to the point, Mamma,' said Brooke with mild irony, long used to her mother's emotional histrionics.

'The point is,' Lillian said, breathing deeply, 'you

don't really care about your sister. You don't want her to marry!'

'What nonsense, though she's happy enough at the moment!'

Louise glanced up sharply and for a second she was the spitting image of her mother. 'Why did you go off with Paul?'

Brooke shrugged, though she felt a stab at her heart. 'I didn't go off with him, dear. It was a one-sided thing really. He went off with me!'

'You ask us to believe that? It's ridiculous!' Lillian cried, her delicate brows almost arched to her hairline.

'He's an extremely odd man.' Brooke forced herself to speak lightly. 'I wouldn't worry your head over him, Lou. He'd only make you unhappy.'

'Let me decide that!' Louise said crossly. 'Your deepest secret is you're jealous of me!'

'We have to blame Mamma for that, dear,' Brooke said evenly. 'You would never have thought of it alone. Besides, didn't you see the way the men were looking at me tonight? I think I looked more than passably attractive.'

'Nigel certainly thought so!' Louise said very bluntly for her.

'We're not talking about Nigel!' Lillian snapped. 'I'm not prepared to waste my breath on Nigel Watling. He's been in love with Louise the longest of all, yet look at the way he behaved tonight.'

'But Mamma, Brooke was leading him on.'

Brooke pressed a hand over her mouth and yawned. 'May this new year bring you a little more sense. Look, we're all pretty keyed up, can't this wait until morning?'

'Tonight should have been wonderful, but you

ruined it for me, Brooke. I'll never forget that!'

Brooke regarded her sister thoughtfully. 'Sometimes I feel a hundred and fifty beside you. It doesn't do to over-indulge children. It's not what they need.'

Louise flushed hotly, her small hands fluttering nervously over her shining blonde hair. 'We invited Paul especially, yet you skulked off with him the moment he arrived.'

'It didn't give me any pleasure, I assure you. Anyway, you kept him prisoner for the rest of the night.'

'What's that?' Lillian said sharply. 'Kept him prisoner? What absolute balderdash! I don't remember your ever being so spiteful. You ran after him, but he wouldn't have you. Poor girl, it's the same old sad story. It's Louise he's interested in, even if he's not good enough for her.'

'I suppose that's why he proposed to *me*!' Brooke retorted, and found herself a chair. 'Hard to believe, isn't it? I promise I'll keep it a dead secret!'

For an instant there was silence, then Louise's strangled gasp.

'What's that you're saying?' Lillian demanded, her blue eyes shining with an unnatural light.

'He asked me to marry him,' Brooke repeated quietly.

'No!' Louise shrieked, and went instantly to pieces.

'What have you been up to?' Lillian asked her younger daughter in a choked voice.

'Watch out, Mamma, I won't be spoken to in that tone!' Brooke yielded to her own anger.

'This is really too much!' Lillian said almost wildly. She sensed that Brooke was telling the truth and the green unflinching gaze brought her late husband painfully to mind. 'What kind of man is he?'

'It's a nightmare, isn't it?' Louise wiped her face with

the back of her hand. The rims of her eyes were red and she looked the picture of suffering.

'You'd best go to bed, child,' Lillian said unexpectedly.

'I haven't the faintest intention of doing that!' Louise cried tormentedly. 'He can drag her off to the altar for all I care, but first I want to know how she did it.'

'I didn't work at it, believe me!' Brooke said dryly.

'You're lying!'

'Watch out.' Brooke put up a hand to the small, flying figure of her sister.

'Pull yourself together, Louise!' Lillian said sharply, and Louise came to an instant halt, rocking on the spot like an automaton.

'Get the truth out of her, Mamma!' Her pretty face, wet with tears, was enough to turn the hardest heart over.

'What did you tell him?' Lillian demanded in a perfectly calm voice.

'It would be better if he looked elsewhere,' Brooke said harshly. 'Perhaps you'd better tell this little fool here that there's no use crying her ardent little heart out. He thinks very kindly of her, but he has no desire whatever to marry her. She should be relieved. I think it's plain enough he's a very ruthless man.'

'All right!' said Lillian, and took a quick turn about the room. 'Are you sure he made himself quite clear?'

'Yes, indeed!' Brooke said dryly. 'Indeed, yes.'

'Just what is your connection?' Louise persisted, blinking her eyes.

'I'm just as surprised as you are!' Brooke said with some patience. 'Actually he put it to me as a business proposition.'

'Ah, that I trust!' said Lillian. Her blue eyes looked away into the middle distance. 'Yes, of course, a business arrangement, a marriage of convenience. He has the money and we have the background. Most certainly that's what he wants at this stage.'

'Apparently!' said Brooke, and let it hang there.

Louise gave another wail and her mother turned on her irritably. 'It will be better if you go to bed, Louise. You'll look all washed out in the morning.'

'I don't understand you, Mamma!' Louise sobbed disconsolately. 'Surely you're not giving this traitor here your blessing?'

'Hush now, darling.' Lillian went to her elder daughter and put an arm around her. 'It would be better if he had asked you because you're the most beautiful little creature in all the world, but the fact is he has asked Brooke and now it's up to us to act sensibly. You'll understand when you think it out.'

'*Never!*' Louise protested. 'You're deserting me for Brooke.'

'I have for the moment.' Lillian didn't deny it. 'Look, darling,' she said with loving patience, 'go along to bed. I'll tell you all about it in the morning.'

'There's no point in discussing anything!' Brooke interrupted flatly. 'I most certainly do *not* want to marry Mr Corelli and I've told him so. There's no need for you to subside into a jelly, Lou. Marry Patrick. He's your only likely recourse, unless you want to find a job.'

Lillian's blue eyes flashed her annoyance. 'I wouldn't find it in my heart to bless this arrangement unless Mr Corelli intends to look after your mother and sister?'

'If I *permitted* him to!' retorted Brooke, feeling

outraged. 'There's no doubt about you, Mamma, you're frightfully adaptable.'

'I have to be,' Lillian maintained with hard clarity. 'Did he say he would restore Wintersweet?'

'There's no point in even discussing it,' Brooke said wearily. 'I'm just as shocked as you are. He's a deep one, Corelli, and about as subtle as a sledgehammer. By the way, did you know he has a sixteen-year-old daughter?'

'What?' Lillian very nearly bellowed, and even Louise flinched.

'One more item of his affairs you didn't know about.'

'So he's been married before?' Lillian demanded.

'I think he's really very fond of her,' Brooke supplied without really answering.

'Where *is* the girl?' Lillian demanded. 'I mean, none of us have ever seen her.'

'She lives in Kenya with his married sister. As soon as he sets up house he's bringing her over. I shouldn't think Lou would have been capable of looking after a teenage daughter.'

Louise breathed deeply and tried to say something, but no words came out. With trembling fingers she pulled her flowered blue silk robe around her, then buried her fluttering hands in the wide sleeves. From shocked resentment she had gone to perplexed incredulity, incapable in her tired state of taking it all in.

Lillian, however, was busy probing deeper into the matter. 'Anyway,' she said, 'there's nothing to worry about, a teenage daughter. Probably she's a very shy, protected little thing. There's school and university and probably a finishing course overseas. No, I think we can safely say we can take a young girl in our stride.'

Brooke felt bound to rouse herself. 'I've already given him my answer, Mamma.'

'You'll soon get over that nonsense!' Lillian said crisply, a frown disfiguring her fine pink and white skin.

'Oh, *no!*' retorted Brooke. 'Even to save the old plantation, I'm not going to tie myself up with Corelli. To put it plainly, he scares me.'

'Naturally he took you by surprise,' Lillian almost cooed soothingly. Her small face lit up and she gave a small chuckle. 'Didn't I always say my girls would save me? Of course we'd want it in writing, a proper arrangement drawn up by a solicitor. I can introduce my little girl to European society. I wager I could even marry her off to an earl. Oh, for goodness' sake, we could take a trip to England, stay at Ashton Hall. It's still in the family.'

'I can see you're not going to listen to reason, Mamma,' Brooke sighed tiredly. 'Would you permit me to go to sleep? I can't keep my eyes open.'

'I'm sorry!' said Lillian with every appearance of a fond mother. 'Louise, come along now. There'll be a higher plateau for you, dear. Don't worry, Mamma will see to it. I've just remembered all the old family connections. We might as well take a trip home at our first opportunity.'

'I don't want to go,' Louise said dully.

'You will, dear, you will!' Lillian clutched her elder daughter to her like a small bird and walked her to the door. Goodnight, Brooke!' she called, glancing over her shoulder. 'He's really a very fine man, you know. I'm sure he's going to make you very happy.'

'You're raving, Mother!' muttered Brooke, picking up a pillow and bashing it nearly senseless.

'No, no, I'm proud of you!' Lillian informed her.

'To think we won't be torn up from our beloved home. To know we won't have to sell off any more of our treasures. Now that you're settled I can give my whole mind to finding someone for Louise. An Italian is all very well, but we all know an English gentleman can't be beaten!'

'Would you mind turning out the light?' Brooke asked in desperation.

'Yes, of course. Goodnight, darling,' Lillian called, 'remember we're on your side!'

She made it sound as if marrying a stranger was a simple operation in logistics. One only had to look at the broad picture, weighing the advantages against the disadvantages, averaging it out until the final picture emerged not too badly at all. There were far worse things than marrying Paul Corelli, it seemed, especially as he was thinking of being generous to his wife's family.

Brooke pulled the sheet over her head, only her red hair emerging. She would drop from hard work before she consented to marry Paul Corelli.

Far from his pressing his suit, a whole week came and went before Brooke saw Paul Corelli again. It had been rather an upsetting time for her with Lillian hurling insults at her after the pleas for pity and compassion had failed. Any grateful, obedient daughter would do as her mother thought best, and even Louise seemed in agreement with this, giving her mother much sympathetic support. As far as Louise was concerned now, it would be much nicer to marry into the English aristocracy than take on Paul Corelli with his uncertain background.

There was a staff meeting on Monday afternoon after

school and when Brooke came out into the quadrangle
she was shocked to see an extravagantly glamorous
Lamborghini pulled into one of the parking bays.

'Good grief, which moneyed father owns that?' Kay
Murray breathed beside her, equally startled.

There was no mistaking the man who slipped out
from behind the wheel managing to look as bold and
dramatic as his car, and Brooke clutched at Kay's arm
almost for protection. 'Stay with me!' she begged.

'I will, dear. I'm truly impressed!'

The other teachers followed them out, making no
better job of not staring than Kay. The car was so
rakish and exciting in design the owner might fully
expect it. Brooke was still clutching Kay's arm when
Paul Corelli closed the space between them.

'*Buon giorno!*'

'How are you?' Brooke asked inadequately, realising
Kay was hanging on for an introduction.

'I'm very pleased to meet you,' said Kay.

'Kay, may I present Signor Corelli, a friend of ...
mine.'

The black eyes mocked her hesitation, but Kay was
very nearly buckling at the knees, not having previously
met a man of Corelli's type. Her reaction was unmistakable and Corelli took it as the normal tribute to
male virility, while inside Brooke seethed. Did he have
to draw so much attention to himself?

'Your mother told me you would be delayed, *cara*,'
he said, 'so I decided to come for you.'

'Excuse me, aren't you lucky!' said Kay. 'I love
your car, Mr Corelli. I don't think I've ever seen such
an exciting machine!' Nor man, was what she plainly
didn't say.

'It's all in the breeding,' he said smoothly.

'And however much money you have. That's my little Volksie over there,' Kay pointed out. 'You won't be joining me this afternoon?' she turned to smile knowingly at Brooke. 'We take turns running our cars,' she explained for Paul Corelli's benefit. 'I bring mine Mondays and Fridays, Brooke the rest of the time.'

'A very sensible arrangement.' He gave her his beautiful smile, and Brooke felt a little nauseated when she saw its effect. Kay, from looking harassed and irritable, had warmed into a pleasant glow.

'I'll see you later, then, Brooke. *Ciao*, Mr Corelli!' Kay flashed a bright smile and ungripped Brooke's arm.

'*A più tardi!*' he rejoined suavely.

'If that means see you later, I'd be delighted!' She wiggled her fingers and walked fast away and when she got to her car she waved.

Corelli waved as well, but Brooke felt as if she had been dropped on her head. 'Were you really speaking to my mother?' she asked moodily.

'Your friend is waving,' he chided her.

''Bye, Kay!' By this time she felt up to it. The Volkswagen rushed down the drive leaving Brooke feeling absolutely deserted unless she appealed to Mr Macmillan, the science master. He was certainly looking their way. She must have even framed his name, for Paul Corelli looked down at her enquiringly.

'*Come dice?* I beg your pardon?'

'Why are you here?' she asked flatly.

'Surely I'm welcome!' He took her arm, steering her gently but implacably towards the powerful Lamborghini.

'Because of you I've had a frightful week,' she said tightly.

'You do look a little pale.' Velvety dark eyes touched her face and her throat and her hair. 'Please can't you tell me?'

'You speak beautiful English, Mr Corelli,' she said tightly, 'but I'm quite certain you think in Italian.'

'I only want to help you!' he responded with such charming sincerity she could have killed him.

He waited until she got into the passenger seat, then he came round to the other side, slipping behind the wheel and turning to examine her averted profile. 'If you like, we'll start all over again, and I'll court you.'

'It would do you no good!' she said, leaning forward to examine the cockpit controls despite herself. She was accustomed to driving her mother's Mercedes and her own mildly luxurious Triumph, but this was something else again.

He caught at her reverent, exploring fingers and held them. 'You must tell me what it is you want. I'm really a very sympathetic type.'

'Do let's go,' she said. 'The Head loves all things Italian. She'll be over here in a moment.'

'God forbid!' He lunged forward and switched on the ignition and within seconds they were gliding down the drive. 'You like teaching, my dear Brooke?'

'I'm not your dear Brooke, and yes, I must say I do.'

'It's not so interesting, I'm told, when one becomes accustomed to it. Say in ten or twenty years. It is perhaps a little severity in you that makes me speak. The scotty little teacher, *no*?'

'Thank you!'

'*Prego*. You're welcome, young lady.'

'Don't you think we might call off all this pretence?' she said.

'You must not say that!' He glanced at her briefly

and shot off at the lights. 'Your mother has warned me you're feeling nervous.'

'My mother is without regard for what I consider the necessary moral considerations. I can't marry a man I don't love, and I'm sure you would be the first to agree you don't love me.'

Something about her tone made him smile. 'You sound regretful, *bambina*. If you feel not loving you is so outrageous you should take good care to make yourself as perfect as possible.'

'Are you ever serious?' She turned her head, seeing the smile on his mouth and the deep cleft of his chin.

'With regard to you, perfectly. I mean to have you and you must have confidence in me.'

'Oh?' she said, and leant her head back against the plush, expensive-smelling upholstery. 'It all seems like a bad dream.'

'Please, do not say that. It is not nice!'

'Have you always been this way?' she asked.

The arrogant dark profile grew haughty. 'My experiences have convinced me a man must reach out for what he wants.'

'Why *me*?' Brooke cried in honest bewilderment, and the shimmer of tears overlaid her golden-green eyes. It had been a terrible week and she was feeling quite lacerated, unable to cope with this fantastic man. It didn't do to let him see he was frightening her, but she was too tired to help it.

'Suppose I tell you.' His voice sounded very deep and melodious, consonants and vowels gliding in to one another, the r's softly rolling ... 'Every man has an idea of a woman he could love, the woman he wants to lie with all through the night, to come home to after the day's work is done, the woman he wants to have near him, to bear and rear his children. It won't hurt you to know you come just a little towards my ideal. You're beautiful, foolish, but intelligent. You make jokes, you laugh—I have seen you. Your eyes sparkle with challenge, defiance. I intend to keep you and I'll never hurt you. You must believe that.'

'That would be kind of you,' she cut in, still out-raged, 'but I don't need you, Mr Corelli.'

'You know that's not so.' His voice had lost its caress-ing quality, tinged now with a hard authority. 'You know you cannot cope on your own. You know you have a deep sense of responsibility to your mother and sister and it would hurt you badly to see your old home pass out of the family.'

'It's no use!' she sighed. 'Everything you say is true, but I can't be bought. I know you have a reputation for ruthlessness, but you can't beat me down. If and when I marry I'll be sure the man I love loves me. Anything else is degrading!'

'Then if it comforts you I will be pleased to make you love me.'

He said it in a way she couldn't imagine anyone else saying; as though it were a simple matter to accomplish her seduction. Glancing at his profile, she was more than ever reminded of some diabolical Ren-aissance prince, inherently ruthless and proud, seeing that all things he wanted fell into his hands.

'Please take me home,' she said, feeling very close to tears.

Unexpectedly he put out a hand and touched her cheek. 'It has been bad for you, *no*?'

'We all say things we regret. I don't admire my be-haviour either. But you must believe me, I can't marry you no matter how many beg and plead.' She closed her eyes for a moment, just remembering the scenes of the past week. 'I don't *know* you. I don't know anything about you except you're rich ...'

'*Very* rich.' His voice dropped mockingly. 'It is easy once one makes money to build on it. First the construction company, then the land deals and so on. I have very many interests now. I have made my reputation, now it only remains to acquire a family and an admirable old house such as your own. Don't shiver like that, there is nothing abnormal about what I'm saying, and I want you for the right reasons. The very first time I saw you I arrived at my plan.'

He looked at her briefly and it was the most intimate glance she had ever received. She knew the colour whipped into her cheeks, and her clenched hands in her lap were unsteady. 'You sound as though I can alter nothing.'

'A takeover, don't you call it?' He spoke with amused arrogance. 'I know you're very modern-minded, very liberated, but you are still a woman with a woman's age-old feelings. Don't you believe in fate?'

'I know certain people can alter the course of one's life, but I'm not going to let you, Mr Corelli. If I struggle I can't be hypnotised. Your eyes are alien to me, very black and deep. You have the irresistible charm of your race, but I'm proof against it. What a pity your instinct didn't lead you to somebody else. Catherine Benton comes from an old and respected family. Rumour had it you were very interested in her.'

'Really?' His accent was very pronounced. 'I took her out to dinner a few times. Does this mean we had to become engaged?'

As he was talking he was moving over into the left

lane to take the next exit and Brooke jerked in her
seat. 'We're going the wrong way.'

'So?'

The sensation of unreality was extraordinary. 'This
isn't a kidnap, is it?'

'I would like you to see where I live.' His voice suggested that this was perfectly ordinary.

'I know where you live,' she said tautly, '"The
Columns".'

'I helped design it and my company built it, of
course!'

'It's a very luxurious place to live,' she said shortly.
'Why change?'

'I've already answered that,' he said with cool bland-
ness. 'Do not be perturbed, I've already told your
mother I was claiming your company for dinner.'

Before she could help herself, Brooke glanced down
at her clothes, a coffee cream linen skirt and an ivory
silk blouse. Both were still beautifully fresh but hardly
suitable for dinner. 'It's the end of a long day,' she said
quellingly. 'I'm not dressed to dine out.'

'*Non importa!*' he said lightly. 'We'll have a small
party of our own on the terrace.'

'How far is it to the ground?' she asked dryly.

'I have the penthouse apartment.' He glanced at her
with sparkling black eyes. 'I would not suggest you
fly away from me like a bird.'

'The idea disturbs me all the same. I will see your
apartment, Signor Corelli, if only to satisfy my own
curiosity, but I will *not* be staying to dinner.'

'I'm sorry, didn't I tell you, we won't be alone. I
have a butler-valet-good friend who looks after me. He
is not a young man, but he is highly competent and I
trust him completely. You may too, *signorina!*'

This was said very dryly and Brooke had the grace to blush. Evidently he didn't intend setting up a seduction scene but probably taking it in stages. She had pitched her determination against him, yet he had the ability to make her feel helpless. Even her overwhelming resentment was fading. Of course he had picked the exact evening when she never felt less like a battle.

She leaned her titian head back and sighed almost languorously, and Paul glanced at her briefly and just smiled.

The next morning Brooke came to the conclusion that he had done absolutely nothing to disturb or offend her but rather charm and endlessly fascinate her. Contrary to her expectations she had enjoyed herself immensely, even if her heart beat fast all the time. The apartment was a miracle of elegance and fastidiousness, even a shade ascetic and brilliantly furnished in the modern idiom with only a few fabulous antiques. Because she was scrupulously honest she had to concede that Paul Corelli had tremendous style and polish, and the building itself, The Columns, was very much admired, quite monumental in its proportions and purity of style. Paul Corelli was a highly complex man and she came to see she had to be very careful with him and very careful to guard herself against his awesome charisma, lest he suddenly reach out and claim her before she had time to realise what was happening.

Gianni, the manservant, had come and gone like a magic slave, preparing a superb dinner and watching them eat it. He seemed completely at home with his employer, more a relative than an employee, for it was obvious he regarded Paul with great pride and affection. Even as he refilled their wine glasses he refilled his own and carried it back to the kitchen, subjecting Brooke to a discreet but highly critical scrutiny. She wished too that she spoke fluent Italian, for then she could have undone the riddle of his remarks. Gianni had been almost as unexpected as his master, for there was something very dignified and well bred about him like a nobleman in disguise.

All through classes Brooke pondered on the evening before, until one of her Maths students suggested she was daydreaming. After that, she tried to pull herself together, but the aura of Paul Corelli clung to her like a second skin. As she often did when she wanted some advice she rang Maggie and they arranged to meet for lunch the next day.

'This is lovely!' Maggie said as she sat down. She looked especially smart in a soft classic dress and a cream straw hat decorated with spring flowers. 'Maud is looking after the shop for me. She's a treasure. She sold the Lord knows how many gold chains this morning—they seem to be in!' Her bright brown eyes roamed with pleasure over Brooke's young face and the flawless creamy matt skin. 'Before the girl comes, tell me what's on your mind.'

'I'd have told you before, but you've been busy with the auction. Wait for it ...'

'Yes?' Maggie leaned forward eagerly.

'Paul Corelli has asked me to marry him.'

'Good gracious!' Maggie looked her astonishment. 'I know he's an irresistible force, but surely you haven't known one another long?'

'I don't know him at all,' Brooke said moodily, her eyes almost as green as her peppermint-coloured dress. 'He's power-mad, or at least he thinks he can decide on a woman and that's the end of it.'

'And how is your mother taking it?' Maggie asked shrewdly.

'Last week was hell. This week I had dinner with him, so Mamma isn't speaking out quite so plainly.'

'And Lou?'

Brooke had to smile. 'Simple envy has given away to relief. It's quite true she wouldn't know how to handle him.'

'Which you are willing to do?'

'No!' Brooke's gleaming head shot up and she gave Maggie a speaking glance. 'He's very charming when he wants to be, very foreign, very compelling. He's shown me his apartment and you'd love it. He has a manservant, by the way, who's very attached to him, but I'm not content to marry a man because he's rich and fascinating.'

'Naturally,' Maggie said dryly. 'Why do you young girls have all the luck?'

'Be serious, Maggie!'

'I'm sorry, dear.' Maggie leaned across and patted her hand. 'Now, what are we going to have? I do believe you've lost weight.'

'The climate has been right for it,' Brooke murmured, glancing down at the menu. 'I don't have to rush if you don't. Wednesday my girls go off to Sports.'

'Yes, I seem to remember.' Maggie too was gazing at the menu. 'I wish I was like you and didn't have to mind my figure. I frequently think our scientists should come up with something to control the metabolism instead of indulging in space travel.' She lifted her head and looked directly at Brooke. 'You know, dear, some would think you the most fortunate girl in the world. He's quite a catch!'

'No doubt,' Brooke tilted her head, her eyes beginning to sparkle, 'but I don't in the least mind passing on my great good fortune. I know nothing about him except the sophisticated veneer. Underneath he may be a dreadful barbarian.'

'Come, come,' Maggie remonstrated, then as the waitress appeared at their table both of them had to take time off to order. 'Thank you!' Maggie handed the menus back with a little smile and the girl walked briskly away. 'Now then, I can't allow *that* to pass!' Maggie said seriously. 'He hasn't done anything to offend you, has he?'

'Nothing beyond asking me to marry him.'

The drink waiter approached and Maggie waved him away. 'Not in the middle of the day. You didn't want anything, did you, dear?'

'No, thank you,' Brooke said absently. 'I don't think, Maggie, he knows how to take no for an answer. There's one other thing, he has a daughter.'

There was silence for a moment and Maggie looked down at her clasped hands. 'Family means a great deal to Italians. Where is the child?'

'She's not a child exactly. She's sixteen and she's living in Kenya at the moment with her aunt, Paul's sister.'

'He must have been very young,' Maggie mused. 'He's only in his early thirties now, isn't he?'

'Thirty-five,' Brooke admitted. She looked at the older woman and there was still a trace of shock in her face. 'He told me very little about it beyond the fact that he wasn't married.'

'Amazing!' Maggie said slowly. 'At least he didn't lie to you. I can't pretend I'm not surprised, but these things happen. Obviously he has custody of the child, or he will have. If you're not going to marry him, I shouldn't worry about it.'

'Mamma will be very upset and angry.'

'I can't understand your mother,' said Maggie. 'Yet you have to hand it to her, nothing deters her. First Louise was the fortunate one, now that he's wisely chosen you, there's nothing to be done about it except you should marry him. Extraordinary!'

'He's promised to support Mamma and Lou in style.'

'And your mother wasn't upset by the suggestion?'

'She can't help it, Maggie,' Brooke said loyally. 'She's had no training for anything except being looked after. If I marry Corelli life will go on for her as it has in the past. Whatever happens Louise won't have to marry anyone she doesn't love.'

'But no one can force you, dear!' Maggie exclaimed, a little shocked in her turn.

'No, but I believe him when he says Mamma will never have to worry again. If I marry him he'll carry out all the restoration work on Wintersweet and we'll live there.'

'Lillian too?' Maggie asked in wonderment.

'I believe he intends to set her up royally elsewhere.'

'And he's right!' Maggie drew a sigh of relief as if she couldn't help it. 'Here I am so absorbed I didn't notice the food arriving. Eat up, child, and relax. There are shadows under your eyes even if they only emphasise their beauty. *I* should accept Signor Corelli in a flash, but then I'm of an age not to worry about dangerous men.'

Brooke recalled herself to the purpose of eating, while a concerned Maggie kept casting little glances over her downbent face. She deliberately spoke of other things, pleasant things, while they were eating, but she could see Brooke was upset and nothing to be done about it.

'I think I'll have to brick myself into a wall to get away from him!' Brooke announced suddenly, looking so angry and amused both of them burst out laughing.

'Nobody wants you to do that,' said Maggie, pressing her instinctive liking and admiration for Corelli. 'Let him take you out, let him spoil you. You deserve to be happier than you are. You have time to decide if you truly can't come to care for him.'

'That's the maddening thing,' Brooke said soberly, and for a second her hand crept to her breast as though to still the striking heartbeats. 'I feel myself moving imperceptibly towards him every moment I spend with him. The other evening was a mistake. I found myself enjoying it too much.'

'You're not usually so timid, dear,' Maggie commented gently.

'Perhaps I'm afraid of a golden cage. Anyway, being a good friend to a teenage girl is quite a responsibility.'

'You handle them very well at school. Miss Richards is very pleased with you, I believe.'

'That's different, Maggie,' Brooke said desolately. 'You like him, don't you?'

'I must confess I do. He's hard-headed, but I'm sure he has a tender streak. He cares about his daughter, why shouldn't he care about you? Living in the shadow of your mother and sister has given you a false idea about yourself. You're a very attractive girl and you have a delightful personality. Don't you think for one moment Paul hasn't noticed this? I'd say he knows very well what he's about.'

'Then your advice is, marry him?'

'Not marry him just like that!' Maggie protested

with faint dismay. 'Get to know him better. Enjoy yourself. Surely he doesn't want to rush you off to a register office on the morrow?'

'I'm sure he's thinking on lines of a big church wedding,' Brooke replied uneasily. 'So is Mamma, and you have to admit Lou would make an entrancing bridesmaid.'

'Adorable,' agreed Maggie, and steeled herself against the delicious sweets trolley. 'When are you seeing him again?'

'He's giving a dinner party on Saturday night. He wants me to meet his friends.'

'And will you?' Maggie kept watching her young friend's strained face.

'I haven't decided.' Brooke's green eyes glinted through her long sweeping lashes. 'When he turns on the charm he can be quite dazzling, but just between the two of us I'm no better than Lou. He petrifies me. I don't want to be dominated. I'm a woman of spirit, I must be independent in thought and action. Much as I love Mamma she's accused me of having no respect for her feelings when I feel she ought to look at it my way. I can't marry just *money*! I'd lose all my dignity, yet Mamma thinks I'm just being argumentative. I detest all our little scenes, and even Lou told me I was being tedious going on about it.'

'Then of course Louise has always taken for granted she would do what Lillian told her without question. You surely understand such a marriage would solve a lot of problems, and you've already admitted he's a very desirable man.'

'Have I?' Brooke seemed too overwrought to argue. 'I suppose he is, but essentially he's a hunting animal, a cat-man.'

'There aren't many left!' Maggie chose to be flippant.

'There's even the danger that I'll rush into his arms completely against my own convictions. I'm not given to dramatics, but honestly, Maggie, that's nearly the way I feel. I hate it when Mamma disapproves of me.'

Maggie wisely said nothing. Lillian would be far from subtle in her treatment of an errant daughter, yet she could detect in her young friend a strange lack of confidence to withstand Paul Corelli. 'Perhaps you're too conscious of his racial heritage, dear,' she said soothingly, 'the charm, the volatility, the sheer physical virility. I realise he's quite a big change from the type of young man you and Louise have been used to, but don't hold it against him. Live your life, every minute of it. Goodness knows, youth is fleeting. I sympathise with you, of course, but I can't help being drawn to your Signor Corelli. My advice is, go along to the dinner party. I can't think of anyone offhand who wouldn't be very pleased and flattered to go. He can't compel you to marry him, and you may discover in him qualities you can admire. In any event, no harm could come of it.' Maggie lifted her face and smiled and after a minute Brooke smiled back, regaining her usual cool self-control.

It wasn't until long afterwards that Brooke was to remind Maggie of her words.

CHAPTER FOUR

THE rest of the week flew past on wings. Brooke was glad she had met Maggie for lunch, for now the question of going to the dinner party was settled in her mind. She had tortured herself for days and now her decision had restored Mamma to high good humour, and that included Louise, of course. Both now turned to her warmheartedly and Brooke revelled in their approval even while she worried about its cause. All Paul had to do was watch and wait. It was a role Brooke thought suited his whole aura, for she couldn't rid herself of her mental picture of him and the notion that she was being stalked with extreme cunning.

On the back seat of the car was her new dinner dress. Mamma and Louise had come in to town especially to help her pick it out. Under no circumstances would Mamma permit a re-run of the beautiful burnished gold, but the dress all three of them had finally chosen was quite lovely in a different way—white, almost virginal, Brooke supposed, and her cheeks flushed. Mamma had been very generous and Louise had told her in her kind, sweet way that it suited her beautifully. Nothing is going according to *my* plans! Brooke thought almost despairingly. She wished she had never laid eyes on Paul Corelli even as she found herself taking the high, winding road that led to the exclusive avenue where he lived.

She steered the car automatically, wondering if he wasn't directing her subconscious as well. It was a

beautiful afternoon and here and there she could
catch glimpses of the heavenly deep blue of the water.
Of course she could always tell herself she was curious
to see The Columns again. The apartment building
had impressed her immediately, just as at one time it
had been quite a talking point in the city. To know
that he had worked closely with the architect and even
suggested the design gave her a feeling of kinship, a
tenuous feeling to be sure, but at least it was there.
Her dear father had been an architect and she had
worshipped him as a small child.

Her thick upturned hair swept her shoulders and
she pushed it back with one hand. She was letting it
grow longer because Maggie had told her it suited
her 'tall, beautifully proportioned body'. Dear Maggie!
she showed her affection in many ways and she had
made a study of building up Brooke's confidence in
herself. It had been rather awful in a way, shooting up
over Mamma and Louise's head and not seeing the
charm of her own slender supple body. Her red hair
she couldn't do anything about. It was too bright a
colour, even if her girls at school frequently told her it
was wonderful. Thinking of them she smiled, for she
couldn't help knowing she was very popular.

She seemed to be alone on the road, admiring the
lovely old homes and the exquisite gardens aglow with
the spring flowering. Shade trees lined the avenue
on both sides, refreshing the eye, and filtering the
dazzling sunlight. She was going quite a bit out of her
way, but she told herself she wanted to see The Columns
again. It was splendid, and certainly the soaring white
columns were classical in design. From the penthouse
one had a magnificent view of the glittering city lights
by night and the shining blue harbour by day. The

dark, ageing Gianni's manner towards his employer was rather endearing, Brooke thought. Probably there was a Story there, as well.

Wattles filled the afternoon with their sweet, heady perfume and there just ahead was the impressive white building she had come to see. She drove on rather slowly, filled with a mingled disquiet and excitement. She was almost like a woman acting under hypnosis. Only a short time ago (she could hardly remember) she had violently declared her dislike of Paul Corelli. Now she seemed almost tied to him.

A dark blue Volvo was parked outside the building and as Brooke cruised nearer two people walked down from the portico and towards the car. Her heart leapt with shock and she stared disbelievingly as she brought the car to a halt outside a Spanish villa with an enormous feathery jacaranda shading the nature strip. Her heart was bumping so much it was making her ill. All she wanted to do was go back the way she had come, but she was compelled to sit there watching the man who had asked her to marry him putting another woman tenderly into her car. She knew the car now, and the woman. It was Cathy Benton, her long dark hair sheened with sunlight, spectacularly dressed, as she usually was. She was in the car now tilting her head to the man who leaned in, unsmiling, but somehow loverlike in his attitude. The whole easy set of his head and body was filled with an animal grace, totally eye-riveting, totally given over to obeying no other law but his own. They looked two handsome, sophisticated people playing sophisticated games with each other.

Brooke couldn't understand why she was so shocked. And she *was*, far more than she had ever been in her life. After all, Paul had been frank with her. He had a child. There had been many women in his life. Probably they threw themselves at him for the most part, but now it seemed to her he was exploiting another human being. *Her!* Heat burned through her body like a flame and the heat of humiliation threatened to engulf her. She had bowed to everyone's persuasion: Mamma's, Louise's, Maggie's, while he was playing the age-old game of two-timing. Whatever it was, fate, or the Guiding Hand of the Good Lord Himself had brought her along this road. She was forced to recognise what manner of man he was; a fascinating and ruthless philanderer.

The Volvo took off smoothly and he was walking back towards the white building, his dark head bent in thought. Even from a distance his dark good looks and lithe grace were striking. He was casually dressed in a blue body shirt and cream slacks and she caught the gold glint of his wristwatch. It was important she move off, yet the most bitter disillusionment sapped her strength. It was no time now to wonder why this seemed like a major disaster. She didn't love him, yet she could scarcely be racked with more all-engulfing emotions. She had said all along that Paul Corelli was trouble, a magnificent trap for a woman. Probably he had abandoned the mother of his child. Probably she was still alive but unable to avenge herself. Caution was a virtue, and she had almost thrown caution to the winds.

A beautiful golden labrador wandered down the drive of the villa, saw Brooke in the parked car and gave her owners a few warning barks. 'Good girl! Look, I'm going!' Brooke gave a little self-deprecating laugh and the labrador, satisfied, turned away. By now, Paul Corelli would be safely inside his very cosy retreat.

Brooke switched on the ignition and put the car in motion, feeling the sudden anger rising up in her.

What a fool he must take her for! What a ninny! Her mouth moved in silent pain. What price fidelity? she thought. A marriage to break down before it had ever begun. A car was moving fairly rapidly behind her and instead of turning she drove straight ahead, her trembling hands exposing her inner turmoil. Why didn't he settle for Cathy Benton and be done with it? She would suit beautifully, though she would be threatened with other women all her life.

Despite herself she couldn't control the quick glance she threw at the front of the apartments. To her further dread Paul Corelli was standing in conversation with another man and they were looking her way. Her heart contracted and she turned her head swiftly, hoping against hope that he failed to recognise her or the car. It was absolutely frightful sometimes to have red hair. Such a colour could never be overlooked, and the paintwork of the Triumph was a bright mustard yellow.

She didn't turn her head and she didn't slow down. She didn't know exactly which way she was going and she didn't really care. Her passionate resentment was an actual pain and she felt immensely ashamed of herself. She should never have allowed herself to come this far. She should never have allowed him a single minute of her time. She had always considered herself a resolute sort of girl with high principles, but like everyone else she too could make a terrible mistake. Nothing would wipe out the sight of Paul Corelli coming out of the building with Cathy Benton by his side. Their names had been linked for quite a while, even while everyone thought he would probably marry Louise. Paul Corelli didn't belong to anyone but himself.

At the intersection she took the turn to the right leading down to a picturesque marina. The sun on the blue water was dazzling and her own eyes green as the sea began to sparkle. She could never belong to a man who could so easily betray her love. But of course she didn't love him, nor he her. But there was honour. It was an enchanting scene, the boats bobbing in the water, a small grove of yacht masts and little rowboats clustering like butterflies. Half a dozen youngsters were standing outside the clubhouse and a young mother was rocking her baby in the green shade.

The road dipped suddenly before the approach to the bridge and in her rear vision Brooke caught sight of the Lamborghini's incredibly elegant bonnet. It seemed to be flowing relentlessly for her, a big powerful car with the driver afire with likely lies and excuses. She put down her foot, just keeping to the speed limit. He could easily overtake her and she only hoped there would be a policeman around to give him a fine.

From out of nowhere an Afghan bounced eagerly out on to the road while its stricken owner gave a high-pitched scream. It had slipped its collar and on this warm beautiful afternoon it was determined on a little fun and a plunge in the blue water. Instinctively Brooke swerved, all thoughts of Paul Corelli fading from her head. Her young mouth was drawn in in panic, but everything was happening too quickly. She *must* right the car while it was skidding out of control. It was never good sense to swerve dangerously for a dog, but she couldn't have done otherwise. The beautiful foolish creature was already at the boat shed while the car was rushing towards the water. Her eyes froze and her young body stiffened, nerves screaming; this was the moment of tragedy and she didn't know she screamed . . .

'Thank God, she's coming out of it!'

The voice was a woman's, low and anxious. Brooke gave a choking cough, consciousness coming back to her in a blinding flash. Her heart was pounding and she was lying face down on the grass with two strong hands hard at her back, just above the waist. There was no more water in her lungs, but she was sick and sore from those pumping hands.

She turned her head weakly, waiting until her vision cleared. 'There now, dear!' A woman on her knees smiled at her and gently pushed the wet strands of hair away from her face.

Brooke tried to speak, but there didn't seem to be any air in her body. Somewhere just beyond her the Afghan stood quietly with its young master, a boy of ten, who barely bothered to brush the frightened tears from his cheeks. Several wary children brightened visibly when Brooke stirred and gave a small moaning sound and on her other side, a police officer in his summer uniform held a subdued conversation with the hurting hands.

'... as well for the young lady you were on hand. Otherwise this could have been a tragedy!'

She heard the answering voice and she gasped in air, choking again, but too weak to resist. A few more breaths, just a few more. She had to keep trying. There was no colour in her face or the mouth that had received the kiss of life. She was exhausted but alive, and directly above her was the man who had dived twice to free her from the submerged car. Strangely she wasn't surprised it was Paul Corelli. He was capable of all kinds of things and he had a strength not given to women.

She felt herself turned and lifted high in his arms

and the carven face above her had a pallor that shocked her, though she wanted to scream at him to let her go. The small circle of people had drawn closer, some speaking gently, trying to soothe and reassure her like the young mother, but she couldn't really hear anything they said; her head rested weakly against Corelli's hard shoulder, as he stood still for a moment while the police officer devoted his attention to getting all the information he required.

'Leave it to me now, sir,' he said quietly. 'You'll want to get your fiancée to a doctor, no doubt, though I'm certain you saved her life. Perhaps you could ring me later on at this number?' He wrote a name and a telephone number on a page of his notebook and pulled it out, folding it neatly and slipping it inside Paul Corelli's shirt pocket. 'I've observed many accidents swerving to avoid animals. Few people do anything else, even though they put their own lives in danger.'

Brooke heard Corelli's deep accented voice thanking the man, then his helpers beyond the police officer's tall, burly figure. His voice sounded harsh yet gentle, its velvety quality scarcely in evidence. Brooke buried her head against him, lost in shock and exhaustion. If Paul had a claim to her now, there was nothing she could do about it. He had succeeded in saving her life, but she could feel nothing, least of all gratitude.

'*Poverina!*' he murmured, as he put her very gently into his car. '*Mia cara*, poor little one!' His voice sounded infinitely tender, as though he held the woman he most desired in his arms. 'What am I to do with you?'

For once she didn't answer but lay completely still, her beautiful skin robbed of all colour, her golden-green eyes darkened to emerald. He went to stroke her cheek and she shrank away from him visibly, sick and a bundle of nerves. All the way back to his apartment there was no other sound but the wind through the window, the dry rustle of leaves. When he lifted her again, she went with him, defeated, overpowered. She was aching and her own heartbeat sounds were like thunder in her ears.

When Gianni opened the door he broke into a stream of Italian that Paul Corelli answered while carrying Brooke easily into the main bedroom. Altered, Gianni dashed ahead to remove the softest, most beautiful velvet spread, but Paul seemed utterly uncaring. He bent over Brooke and she made a soundless little exclamation, her limbs trembling in a spasm. There was a perplexing wildness to her thoughts and her head was almost cracking.

Paul Corelli stood by the bed stroking her hair back, speaking to her now in a soft yet commanding tone of voice. His large, lustrous eyes were blacker than night, blacker than the deeps of the water. 'Gianni has gone for the doctor,' he said soothingly. 'She lives in this very building. She and her husband are good friends of mine, both of them doctors. I feel you need something to settle those nerves—a sedative, then complete privacy to sleep. I will ring your mother, of course. I have no wish to frighten her, but she must be told.'

'I want to go home,' Brooke said worriedly.

'*No!*' His voice sounded vibrant with sudden tension. 'That was a very close brush with tragedy. You must stay here. Adriana is on hand and she will know how to treat you. Afterwards I will certainly take you home to your mother. Have no fear, little one. I do not wish to add to your unease!'

He had locked her green gaze and Brooke shut her eyes to block the sight of him out. Still he remained there, standing over her, holding one of her trembling hands firmly, until the woman he called Adriana arrived.

'Paul, *caro*, what is this I hear?'

The voice was a melodious contralto and Brooke opened her eyes with an effort and tried to sit up. There was no clarity to her thoughts or her vision and the liquid Italian voices passing to and fro became harder and harder to concentrate on. The woman was handsome, but not young, and it soon became evident she knew what she was about. Paul and the agitated Gianni were shepherded from the room, then Doctor Adriana Bonetto turned back to her patient, her dark eyes full of a sympathetic concern.

'Poor child, what an experience! You must be in a nervous state, yet what a miracle Paul was on hand. He is like an eel in the water and he has never lacked courage!' She came over to the bed and cast an intent, professional glance over Brooke's near-ashen face. 'I am here to help you, my dear. Paul has spoken to me often of you. First, I will give you something to settle the nerves, then we will get you out of those wet clothes.'

'Thank you!' Brooke whispered, and the woman, Adriana, gave her a beautiful, understanding smile.

When Brooke awoke, she jerked upright in alarm, her heart pounding. Her hands came up to shield her face and her near-brush with death took on new, terrifying proportions. Dimly she heard her own voice crying out something unintelligible and she put her head down further into her hands, her breath coming sobbingly.

She was in no pain, her dizziness had vanished, but she was still a little close to hysteria. The bronze and crystal lamp on the table beside her was aglow and there was soft, muted light coming from pinlights recessed in the panelled ceiling. She could not have borne the dark just then. Anything was better than the appalling black mantle of darkness upon her.

Some instinct made her lift her head a fraction of a second before the door opened. She sat up straighter, her whole body as taut as a bowstring, one lacy strap of the nightgown she was wearing falling off her sloping shoulder. Nervously she adjusted it while Paul Corelli walked towards her, the lights flickering oddly over the dark, aquiline mask of his face.

'You woke and you were frightened?' He looked down at her, his voice almost taut.

'I'm all right now,' she said faintly, looking so fragile and distressed he came right to the side of the bed, towering above her.

'Shall I call Adriana? She won't mind in the least coming.'

'No.' Her eyes were clinging to his as though hypnotised. He was fully dressed, his ivory silk shirt a sheened contrast to his darkly olive skin, and she wondered in agitation what time it was. Her enormous green eyes flew around the room searching for a clock. The colours were sombre, cream, black and gold, but the furnishings were rich with two exquisite oriental panels decorating the wall on either side of the great antique armoire. There was a wonderful gilded bronze sculpture of a horse, but no clock.

'What time is it?' she asked fretfully. 'I must go home.'

Her wide eyes held shimmering reflections of the

light and more than ever she reminded him of a small trapped creature of the wilds. 'It's almost three o'clock in the morning,' he said with a faint, brittle edge to his beautiful voice.

'It can't be!' She sounded utterly disoriented, disbelieving, and for answer he turned his wrist abruptly for her inspection, the gold face of the watch gleaming in the lamplight. 'I can't see!' she didn't even glance at it and for the first time colour flared into her creamy petalled skin. 'It doesn't matter anyway. I want to go home.'

Her titian hair sprang away from her face like fire and fanned out over her bare shouders and her tender young breasts thrust against the silky covering nightgown. She was trembling uncontrollably and what she was afraid of was happening. The tears came to her eyes and ran down her cheeks.

'Please don't cry!' he said, his lithe body tensing.

'I'm sorry. I'm sorry!' She folded her arms across her and began to rock herself. She didn't hear him move away, neither did she hear him return with his big-catlike tread.

'Drink this.'

'I don't want it!'

'*Drink it!*' he repeated, and guided the glass to her mouth. Her hand was trembling so much his own hand closed over her wrist and she drank down the fiery liquid if only to be free of his grasp.

He appeared to sense it, for he stood up and away from her instantly. 'That should help you sleep, and when you wake again you will feel better.'

Brooke bit her softly rounded lower lip, her eyes very green in her creamy face. 'I'm afraid of you.'

'I know that.'

'I want to leave right away.'

'You don't look nearly well enough!' he said crisply as though that resolved the matter.

'Why didn't my mother come for me?' she demanded, the effect of the brandy serving to relax her as well as bring back a shadow of her former spirit.

'She did come, *piccola*,' he said dryly, 'only you were fast asleep. Adriana was able to set her mind at rest and she was quite satisfied to leave you until morning. Apparently she trusts me where you do not!'

With his eyes lingering on her she tensed, for the first time conscious of the delicate fragility of her night-dress. Adriana had found it for her without bothering to tell her it had been intended as a present for her married daughter. There was a matching robe somewhere and her eye sought for it.

'Lie still, little one. Just lie still and go back to sleep. I promise I'll return you to your mamma first thing in the morning.'

'I'm awake *now*!' she said with faint hauteur.

Unexpectedly he smiled at her tone, and a deep physical pain began to blur all her other impressions. Paul had the beautiful white teeth of his race, the flashing smile that lit his dark features. Knowing what she knew about him he couldn't force her to stay. Probably if Adriana had opened that armoire she would have found some exquisite froth of lace and chiffon hanging beside his robe.

'Why did you ever ask me to marry you?' she burst out with the pain.

'Because I want you!' he said so demandingly she felt the blood course through every inch of her body.

'I don't think that's good enough!' she said bitterly. 'I know I suit your plans, but I have plans of my own.

They don't include you, who appear to want every woman you see!'

'Little fool!' he said urgently. 'Nothing could be further from the truth. I am going to leave you now as I seem to be upsetting you. Let yourself relax and you will sleep.'

'I'm going *now*!' she said stubbornly, remembering every tortured minute of the afternoon. She could see the robe now draped over a carved corner chair and in a moment of recklessness she slid out of the huge bed, intending to make a rush for it. There was a moment of such weakness she almost fainted, then Paul swept her up into his arms, his black eyes narrowing over her, rejecting her defiance. Her heart was beating fast and she was burningly aware of his strong arms and body and the arrogant dark face above her. He was the hunter, the thrill for him was in seduction and her emotions and her jealousy made her struggle in his arms, though she was very dizzy.

'If you persist in doing that you will feel even more terrible!' he said abruptly. 'Where did you get this idea that I am wicked?'

Brooke gave a funny little laugh out loud. 'I thought you hadn't seen Cathy Benton in ages?'

''*Allo!*' he muttered, and glanced down at her, 'you're jealous!'

It hit a raw nerve, but Brooke didn't mind because the adrenalin rushing through her veins made her feel better.

'Put me down!' she said icily.

'Why?' He held his glance on her face, lowering it to the curve of her breast. 'You're my fiancée!'

They were both angry, yet he gathered her to him with assurance and faint violence. 'No, *thank* you!'

she returned vehemently. 'I'd rather be an old maid!'

'Come now, be reasonable!' he said mockingly. 'What do you really have against me?'

'Your adventures!' she whispered, staring up into his face. 'Your affairs and all that. I don't intend to put Positively No Trespassing on my future husband, but I would expect him to be faithful. It's not an unique asset, you know. Husbands are faithful even today.'

'I can hear you!' he said with arrogant serenity. 'Okay, why not? I, too, can be faithful, so don't make difficulties. If something should happen that could make me desire you, then by the grace of God, I should do my very best.'

'I'm sorry, it's impossible!' She said it like a sigh because out of nowhere came a hot, hungry yearning, a demanding to be loved and understood. Always deep within her she had guessed at his attraction, the brilliant blinding force that could crumple her defence and defeat her.

His face seemed completely void of expression, the light on his eyelids, the sculptured mouth and the cleft chin giving him the appearance of a classical statue. 'You want me to love you, don't you?'

'Oh, go away!' she sighed, averting her head from danger. 'Go away and leave me in peace!'

He carried her the few extra feet to the bed, and she kept her eyes tightly closed, while her blood kept singing and urging. It must be shock, she thought. The reaction to a terrifying experience and she still hadn't thanked him.

'There's nothing you want?' he asked in a voice that made her heart flip over.

'Did you have to drive like a madman?' she accused him unjustly.

His shadow fell across her and she opened her eyes, seeing him through her fringed lashes. She could tell he was angry and something else. Something she had evoked.

'You had to rush away like a silly little child!'

'Oh, never mind!' she half groaned, and threw herself sideways, her heart hammering loud and fast.

'What happens now, I wonder? Do you thank me?' he enquired.

'How crazy!' Brooke was breathing hard and he turned her all the way back into his arms, the piercing shock of it making her go limp, while he lowered his head and kissed her softly and deeply on the mouth. It was perfect, and she was aware he was treating her with an unheard-of gentleness, even a tenderness that was more ravishing, more confusing than a hard passion.

When it was all over she still didn't believe what had happened. Waves of despair were coming for her like the tide, but there was an explanation for it. Paul was simply a man with an infernal, sexual radiance, a technique that could drive a woman up to the summit, only to let her fall again like a discarded pebble.

'Buona notte, mia cara,' he said dryly. 'I expect you will fall straight to sleep and dream of me.'

'No. Oh no!' she exclaimed 'I'm not that sort of a dreamer!'

'Actually you kiss beautifully!' The faint laugh in his voice mocked her. 'I'm yearning for our next!'

'Goodnight, Mr Corelli!' she said. 'The best thing you could do is continue your promising friendship with Cathy. It will save you a lot of trouble.'

'I've had trouble all my life,' he said smoothly, 'and I'm not going to lose my best piece of property yet.

Fall asleep on it, *cara*, because I know how to handle you!'

At this point Brooke was so overcome with her feelings she buried her bright, tumbled head in the pillows, ruining the effect of cool determination she had been trying to maintain. She heard him mutter something to himself in Italian and there and then she decided to take up the language. She had been reasonably successful with French and German.

'You aren't crying, *piccola*, are you?' he asked at the door.

'Sure. For *you*!' she called to him ironically. 'It's a pity to knock down your dream house.'

'You'd never do that, not you!' he returned coolly, and discreetly shut the door.

The wild desire seized her to fling something after him. The taste and the scent of him was still on her mouth, clinging to her skin. Nervously she touched her pulsing, sensitised mouth; the short curving upper lip, the full rounded curve of the lower lip with the faint indentation at the centre. If she had ever wondered whether woman was lovingly created for a man's pleasure, her own feelings were answer enough. With just one perfectly controlled kiss Paul had destroyed all her prefabricated resistance. She no longer knew what was true or untrue, good or bad, right or wrong. She only knew he could excite her unbearably, leave her no peace unless she buried the memory of that brief caress in her subconscious. Her accident had made her vulnerable, the witching unreal hour she had woken. And then, to be in his bed, an impossible place to block him out. She must have sleep. Time to think. He could scarcely keep pursuing her.

Her slender limbs relaxed and she fumbled for the

other pillow, pushing it under her head. She would never give up this idiotic fight. So now she was sleeping in his bed, but for different reasons from anyone else. His behaviour was inexcusable, incurable; he was too attractive to women. Brooke ran her fingertips along the incredibly smooth sheet. It was a long way to the other side. There was a small tightening of excitement in her throat, and she reproached herself sleepily. Paul Corelli might make an infinitely artistic lover, but she was protected by her moral scruples. Her whole being was given over to headlong flight, but though she might try hard to run away from it, he *had* saved her life. The crowded darkness of her thoughts seemed full of him. It was rather sad, but it was too late. Sleepily she whispered his name and stopped in an instant. It would be a little miracle to escape him, but she had always had a rebellious nature.

Six minutes later when the French clock in the living room struck four, Brooke was fast asleep, with the sweet traitorous taste of his kiss on her mouth.

CHAPTER FIVE

HER near-fatal accident left Brooke curiously vulnerable for almost a month, at the end of which time Lucia Corelli arrived from Kenya via London in the care and company of a female relative.

'You must meet her,' Paul said in his beautiful accented voice that cut her like a knife.

For the past weeks it had seemed easier not to avoid him and Lillian was delighted, as gay and enthusiastic as once she used to be when Grandfather was alive. Paul seemed to be always in and out of the house until finally Brooke asked him waspishly whether he was actually courting her mother. She was too conscious of his charm, of his truly Latin gallantry. Even Louise seemed in tremendously high spirits, just waiting for the day she would meet and conquer a British earl. It was so absurd Brooke hoped fervently that some worthy young man would present himself soon—a determined young man who wouldn't let Lillian frighten him away. Paul Corelli was not at all the kind of man to be intimidated by a woman, not that it mattered, for Lillian 'adored' him and seemed to take it as a *fait accompli* he would marry Brooke very quickly.

The extraordinary thing was, although he frequently invaded their home bringing flowers and wine and Lillian's favourite Swiss chocolates he never once mentioned marriage to Brooke, treating her to the same warm, suave friendliness he showed to her mother and sister; in fact he seemed to prefer Lillian. The few oc-

casions he had taken Brooke out alone in the evenings
his manner could never have been described as seductive, rather deeply courteous, and cool. He told her the
morning after her accident that he had no idea Cathy
Benton would call on him. She had certainly not been
invited, neither had she ever been inside his apartment
alone, but Brooke was incapable of believing him. She
didn't even blame Cathy, for he was immensely sensuous, let alone rich and clever. Probably Cathy had
fallen genuinely in love with him. Louise said so, and
Cathy was more Louise's friend than hers. Well, his
riches and good looks made no impression on Brooke
and she refused stubbornly to admit to even the slightest infatuation.

Meanwhile Lillian was ecstatic. On that particular
day Paul had bought back for her a Kang Hsi late
seventeenth-century Chinese blue and white porcelain
dish that had always stood on its stand in the breakfast
room. 'Isn't he *sweet*?' Lillian cried, and sat down
opposite Brooke, motioning to her to pour out another
cup of coffee.

'I suppose so,' Brooke returned dubiously. 'He's not
my type.'

Lillian threw back her pretty head and laughed. 'You
and your jokes! It's as Paul says, you think something
quite different.'

'What are we going to do about Lucia?' Brooke
asked.

'Why not give her a party?' Lillian said gaily. 'It
would be a problem trying to get a lot of people in
Paul's apartment, why not here? Wintersweet is ideal
and she'll be staying here when she's not at boarding
school.'

'We haven't met her yet!' Brooke answered soberly.

'She may be already a woman. The Latin races mature quickly, don't they? She may not be at all what we're expecting.'

'What matter?' Lillian asked impatiently. 'All girls like a party, don't they? It would be the very least we could do after all Paul's many kindnesses, and he sounds absolutely devoted to her. He told me he's only seen her twice, very briefly, in the past four years. Poor little thing! Her aunt sounds a warmhearted woman, but there's no substitute for a parent's love.' A tear stood in Lillian's eyes and she blinked it away. 'Has he spoken to you of the child's mother? I'm too sensitive to ask.'

'Only once,' Brooke said truthfully. 'I think the whole subject is too painful.' As well it might be, she thought but didn't add. Most people would assume Paul had been married before and she intended to let it go at that. It was none of her business in any case and she felt protective of the young Lucia and bound to keep silent. Only Maggie knew, and Maggie had never been known to betray a confidence.

As it happened Paul called to ask whether he might bring Lucia and his distant cousin, Carla, over to meet them. Knowing her mother would certainly say yes, Brooke suggested that they might all like to come to dinner the following evening and he rang off, leaving his mellifluous words of gratitude in her ears. Not only did he seduce the eyes, she thought crossly, but his voice fell vibrantly on the ear, not unlike the voice of an Italian actor she had always admired. Or had her mother brought that to her attention? Lillian, too, was very susceptible to voices, and these days she looked very pretty and relaxed as though the worries of the world had been lifted from her slight shoulders.

Brooke flatly refused to call caterers in and offered to prepare the dinner herself. Both Lillian and Louise shied away from the kitchen. Grandfather had always had a housekeeper and household staff, but those days were long gone. Anyway, Brooke told herself, she liked to cook, although she didn't intend anything complicated. Later on in her life she thought she would like to take up gourmet cooking as a hobby. Fine food presented with imagination naturally appealed to her as a woman and she got as much pleasure from preparing a dish as from actually eating it. In the end, after a brief discussion with her mother, she settled on a seafood appetiser with one of the Mt Pleasant dry whites, then a well seasoned beef casserole, served with fluffy white rice, garlic bread and plenty of tossed green salad. That way she could relax with the casserole prepared ahead and the rum cream pie her friend Kay, at school, called 'scrumptious!' There was plenty of wine in the cellar. Grandfather had been something of an authority on wine and she was sure if she looked she would find a dozen of the beautiful Mildara Cabernet Sauvignon '63, a superb example of a dry red. They could have cheese to follow if anyone wanted it; Brooke always liked a Camembert herself. In a way it was quite exciting to prepare this little dinner party and she was anxious to make Paul's young daughter feel welcome to her new country.

About half an hour before their guests arrived, Brooke went downstairs to check the dining room. It looked particularly beautiful at night. Brooke had grown up with antiques and she had formed her opinions early. She loved them and their permanence. She didn't care at all about status symbols, but she realised the room still held some beautiful, valuable pieces like the mahogany dining room suite with its matching chairs that had been made to comfortably seat forty people and which would only fit into a house the size of Wintersweet. Of course the table wasn't fully extended and a good many of the chairs were up in the attic, but there was a feeling of absolute rightness about the room.

In the mirror of the large mahogany bow-fronted sideboard she caught her own reflection. The ill-fated white gown she had bought for Paul's dinner party he had insisted on replacing, so charmingly adamant no one allowed her to say no. She was wearing it tonight, a one-shouldered classic white gown that made the most of her tall, slender figure and for some reason made her hair look flamboyantly beautiful. There was no doubt about it, he had a great sense of clothes and she was sure many women had benefited.

Grandfather's magnificent gilt bronze *surtout de table* comprising a pair of candelabra, a pair of dessert baskets and a neo-classical centrepiece graced the long gleaming table and in the urns surrounding the base and the baskets held aloft by beautiful gilt bronze maidens Brooke had placed the most perfect white camellias she could find. The Storr silver Mamma had sold, but some superb examples of Minton porcelain in the Sèvres manner occupied its place on the mahogany sideboard. The late Regency chandelier above her head lit the room to a soft brilliance. Once Mamma had made an attempt to clean it herself and come to such grief they had to call in the professional they should have called in in the first place. Even the smallest chandelier had a surprising number of pieces in it, and the dining room chandelier was almost a densely packed glass tent over ninety centimetres high.

Brooke was just staring up at it admiringly when her mother swept into the room, clapping her hands with all the innocent pleasure of a child.

'Beautiful, darling! You're really very artistic, but make sure you get those camellias out of the baskets afterwards.'

'I will, Mamma,' Brooke answered dutifully. 'You look very soignée.'

'Thank you, dear,' Lillian said complacently, and put a hand to the back of her newly styled hair. 'Not too short, do you think?'

'No, very youthful. You don't look a day over thirty-eight.'

'Yes, I'm in perfect health, thank God, and I always get my full quota of sleep. At twenty I was devastatingly lovely—even more so, I think, than my sweet Louise. By the way, dear, you're looking very elegant yourself. I always said being in love puts a special bloom on a woman.'

Brooke could have scorned that in her case, but she didn't. Her mother was looking particularly happy, like a little girl who would never grow out of her dream world, and there was no point in spoiling her evening. A little later Nigel and Patrick arrived and Louise in her favourite jacaranda blue hurried out alone to meet them. They had been invited to improve the male/female ratio and Lillian held to the concept of the more good-looking men, the merrier.

Out in the kitchen she checked on the dinner while Louise offered the boys a pre-dinner drink. They had all of them known one another since childhood and it wasn't difficult for them to find plenty of things to talk about. Nigel, drink in hand, wandered out to the kitchen to say hello to Brooke. He had taken her

sailing twice over the past couple of weeks and they
had enjoyed themselves immensely. Nigel when he
wasn't trying to be James Bond was very engaging, and
tonight he looked quite strikingly attractive.

'Got the car back yet, pet?' was the first thing he
asked.

'Only just!' Brooke gave a little convulsive shiver.
'Paul took care of everything. There was quite a bit of
damage to the front end and the parts were hard to
get, so he had them flown out from England.'

'Ah, the joys of being a millionaire!' said Nigel, advancing to the centre cooking island and looking admiringly at everything. 'You didn't do *this*, did you,
darling?'

'All in a day's work!' she said blithely. 'Mind you,
I did cheat a little with the extra numbers. That pastry
I couldn't resist at Otto's. It was very expensive but
worth it. That delicious rum cream pie, as you guessed,
is mine.'

'What else?' Nigel drained his Scotch and soda.

'Beef casserole, hot garlic bread, a mountain of
steaming fluffy rice and a green tossed salad with the
dressing as the Italians make it!'

'Brilliant!' Nigel said appreciatively. 'Not only a
natural cook but a brain as well.'

'Seafood to start!' said Brooke, hurriedly dipping
her fingers under the tap and wiping her hands. 'Can I
hear voices?'

Nigel made a sort of mad grimace and glanced backward over his shoulder. 'We'd better go out. Better
let me untie your apron, sweetie. It quite spoils the
silken image.'

He came behind her, but instead of untying the
apron he put his hands round her waist and nuzzled

her cheek. 'Hmmm, heavenly! What is it, My Sin?'

'You're not terribly good—it's Caline, Jean Patou!'

'The very thing!' said Nigel, emboldened by the drink in him and the party atmosphere. 'Do you want to hear what I think?'

'No,' Brooke said briefly, wondering if she should try a tiny scream.

'O.K.' Nigel didn't appear to want to take no for an answer. 'It's my bet you're thinking of Corelli as a future husband.'

'In which case you might let go of her!'

The door had opened and Paul stood on the threshold, smiling in a manner that didn't reach his eyes and carrying a number of beautifully wrapped gifts.

'It's my fault. I'll admit it!' Brooke said sweetly, looking sideways at Nigel and feeling in the mood for mischief.

'Thank you, Nigel,' Paul said pleasantly, and Nigel didn't have to take a second glance at him to get the idea.

'Don't keep us waiting, you two!' He closed the door behind him and for an instant there was silence in the room.

'We might as well go out,' Brooke said briskly. 'May I get by?'

'*Mi scusi!*' He bowed, put his parcels down on the sideboard, but as she went to sweep past him he caught her high up on the arm.

'What is it?' she asked, a little bewildered by the faint trace of savagery that prowled in his black eyes.

'No use to look to Watling!' he told her pointedly. 'You are not yet my dear fiancée, but he had better stay away from you, and you make sure you tell him this.'

'You're joking!' she answered tautly, her green eyes flicking all over his face.

'*No!*' he shrugged, looking very foreign, and anyone else but Brooke might have decided she had better take his advice.

'Here's to a nice evening,' she said with false gaiety. 'If you'll come through I'll have the chance of meeting your daughter.'

'Of course you are right.' His hand fell away from her arm and she just knew there was going to be a bruise there. She had to thank him for so many things, including the small treasure trove he had just put down on the sideboard, but some deep-seated resistance within her prevented her.

'You look very striking this evening!' he said in a suave, formal tone. '*Una bella ragazza.*'

'You made no mistake with this dress!' she said, matching the odd, formal tone.

'No!' he agreed dryly. 'Now you look as beautiful as you're stubborn. Come, little one, so I may introduce Lucia and Carla. Lucia badly needs a young friend to turn to.'

Something very gentle in the words broke down her hostility. Something about him frightened her, caused a slight fluttering of the heart. In a very short time he seemed to have changed the whole course of her life, plunging her into a world of intrigue and a dangerous emotional involvement, yet she saw from the expression in his brilliant dark eyes that he loved his daughter and wanted the best for her. In a small way it put her most definitely on his side.

In the drawing room everyone seemed to be standing about like statues obviously waiting for them and watching their progress.

'Ah, darling!' Lillian cried with just the faintest touch of anxiety. 'Do come and meet Lucia and Carla!'

At her mother's side, Louise raised her delicate eyebrows faintly at her sister, then Paul took over, performing introductions.

Not for a second did Brooke betray her deep surprise. With Paul such a striking-looking man, so eye-catching in every way, she had expected Lucia to be a true Mediterranean beauty, perhaps even already a woman as Brooke's own class at college were still very much schoolgirls, but Lucia was physically and temperamentally as different from her father as she could be. She was painfully shy, very small and slight, at first glance plain until one noticed her beautiful gentle eyes and the wealth of glossy dark hair that was unbecomingly styled for her small, narrow face.

'How are you, Lucia?' Brooke said softly to the top of the glossy head. 'I've so been looking forward to meeting you!'

At this Lucia lifted her head shyly, and her dark eyes grew bright and expressive. 'It is very kind of you. Papa is right, you are most beautiful. *All* of you!' She turned, embracing Lillian and Louise with her eyes.

'You sweet child!' Lillian took the girl's hand and patted it as Carla and Brooke acknowledged one another. For one ghastly minute at the front door Lillian had very nearly made a dreadful mistake, mistaking Carla for Lucia until she could see better in the light. Not that Paul looked remotely like anyone's father, let alone a grown woman, but Carla was much more in the expected mould, a sophisticated and confident young woman secure in her own slightly lush good looks.

She focused her big dark eyes on Brooke and looked her up and down, not correctly, but with intense critical appraisal, and though Brooke felt the jolt of surprise she kept on smiling as she murmured a few pleasantries. Having decided that Brooke was somehow unsuitable, Carla let her eyes travel to Paul's sculptured face, the brown glitter melting to liquid, the flamingo tips of her fingers barely touching his sleeve.

Aha! Brooke thought wryly, and saw the flash of agreement in her sister's eyes. Carla was busy telling them how kind Paul had been to her and what good friends they had been years ago in Kenya. Nigel, a little distant from Louise, was looking secretly amused, but the blond-headed Patrick seemed attracted by the flashing vitality of Carla's golden-skinned face. That Louise was observing him and his betraying expression didn't seem to matter. Though she had other plans, Louise still clung obstinately to her admirers and anyone could see Carla di Campo was a potentially dangerous woman.

Over dinner Brooke received many more hard, assessing glances from Carla's dark eyes. She was not beautiful as many people supposed at first glance, but she was undeniably attractive, with strongly marked features, a sensuous mouth and a provocative figure bordering on the very slightly plump. She didn't waste much time charming the women, including her 'little mouse of a cousin', but she laughed frequently with Nigel and Patrick and she didn't bother keeping her devouring eyes off Paul, every little reminiscence implying that they had known one another very well indeed in Kenya. Rather maliciously Brooke met Paul's bland, sardonic gaze, but she could detect no hint of discomfort in him.

If Carla wished to make it appear they were very good friends, her attempts were being reduced to the respectable by his manner.

The food, to Brooke's gratification, was very good. Everyone helped themselves liberally to everything while Lillian commended her aloud on her efforts, allowing Paul to refill her wineglass with some of the beautiful Cabernet Sauvignon. Ordinarily Brooke hardly drank red wine, but the beef casserole was so delicious. Carla, who seemed hungry, told them *she* was a brilliant, natural cook, and Nigel retorted that he wouldn't be afraid to let her prove her claim some evening soon.

All of them, with the exception of Carla who was offhandedly affectionate, were very gentle with Lucia, not trying to draw her out but giving her time to eat quietly and enjoy the conversation. Her intensely dark, heavily lashed eyes almost swamped her small face and she was wearing a dress in a shade of green that made her olive skin look sallow. Carla, in her flamingo-coloured silk jersey, couldn't have presented a greater contrast and Brooke wondered why Carla hadn't gone to the trouble of finding a more becoming dress for Lucia to wear. Brooke was relieved to see Lucia's skin was smooth and clear, and with her glossy dark hair cut short and allowed to curl naturally she could look appealing.

The meal progressed and as Brooke brought the coffee in she caught Paul's look of amused admiration. Their glances locked and he smiled, black eyes softening to velvet, his teeth very white against his dark, polished skin. Hastily she looked away from him, but not before she noticed Carla was regarding both of them with a hawk eye. Paul got up to assist her and afterwards, Brooke thought wryly, it had turned into a very successful dinner party with everyone in excellent spirits, induced by the food and the wine and their beautiful surroundings.

It was after eleven o'clock before anyone thought of going home, and Brooke was betrayed briefly when Paul drew her to him and lightly kissed her mouth. Lucia coloured shyly and smiled as though it was only a matter of time before her father and Brooke would be married, but the blood racing under Carla's cheeks might very well have been anger.

Louise thought it was and scarcely waited until their guests had gone to murmur it in Brooke's ear.

'She's jealous, I can tell!'

'Poor little girl!' said Lillian, looking back at both of them. All three cars were slipping down the drive and out into the secluded, tree-lined street. 'I've never been so embarrassed in my life. To think Paul could have such a plain daughter! I very nearly made the mistake of thinking Carla was she. By the time she got into the light of course I realised my mistake, but I'm quite sure Paul noticed. He doesn't miss a thing!'

All three of them walked back into the entrance hall and Brooke shut the heavy wide door flanked by arching windows and a fanlight of very beautiful etched glass. 'I think it was successful all the same. She's actually a very sweet and modest young girl.'

'Terribly *shy*!' Lillian commented, switching off the outside lights. 'Which is scarcely the case with Miss di Campo. I wonder if it mightn't be an idea if you and Paul get married right away.'

'It all seems so splendidly romantic!' Louise maintained, lost in a daydream.

'Pretty foolishly romantic, don't you mean?' Brooke returned rather sharply.

Lillian gave a delicate, muffled little yawn. 'Please, darling, don't continue your revolution. I'm sure your heart is in the right place. Paul will make a better world for all of us and that little girl will be lost if someone doesn't come to her assistance. She can't possibly wear her hair like that or dress so drably. I mean, Paul is so *elegant*. His clothes are so beautiful, uniquely European in flavour, yet Lucia couldn't have worn a more unbecoming dress—and in such a colour! It emphasised the sallow tone of her skin.'

'Carla could have given her some good advice,' Brooke permitted herself the waspish comment, 'but she doesn't seem to feel anything at all except for herself and Paul.'

'I personally would marry him right away!' said Lillian. 'Now, darlings, I'm going to bed. Louise, lend your sister a hand.'

'As long as that doesn't mean washing up!' Louise protested, looking at her small, pretty hands.

'Which just goes to show when you were last in the kitchen!' Brooke said dryly. 'We have a dishwasher, remember?'

'Well, I've seen you washing up at different times.' Louise frowned in puzzlement.

'When I choose to,' Brooke agreed. 'It's not economical to use the dishwasher all the time.'

But Louise scarcely heard, as she walked into the kitchen and exclaimed over the gifts Paul had left.

In the morning Paul rang to thank them for a delightful evening and Lucia and Carla were given their chance to say thank you too. Brooke took the call as neither her mother nor Louise were early risers, and never after a night of entertaining. By the time she got to school she had stopped seething over the artificial friendliness in Carla's voice, obscurely glad that Lucia had an apartment to herself which Carla was sharing. It seemed strange that Carla had been chosen as a companion for Lucia. So far as Brooke could judge they didn't have a thing in common and Carla seemed faintly dismissive in her attitude to her own sex, drawn very strongly towards men and showing it. Or rather, *a* man: Paul Corelli.

Brooke found herself brooding on it all day. From time to time the fear shook her coldly that she was giving in to the many advantages marriage with Paul Corelli would bring. She would be mistress of her own home, Wintersweet, Mamma and Louise would be absolutely secure and she knew in her heart that if she allowed him to make love to her she would be carried away by a dangerous passion. He was incredibly persuasive and she might even end up thinking it would be the height of foolishness to turn down his offer. Carla had arrived and Brooke's first instinct was right. Carla at some time had been in love with him, still was, and the knowledge gave her a very uncomfortable sensation.

As for Lucia——! Brooke had felt her heart go out to her. She needed guidance and a warm understanding. Probably she had been miserably lonely without her father and naturally very retiring. Brooke wondered whether she knew the circumstances of her birth and whether they had altered her and made her a different person. If not, she could only resemble her mother, and Brooke had a shattering fear that she might still be alive. Much as she deplored going into the matter she really did have to know about Lucia's mother. It didn't even occur to her then that she had been lured into an inescapable position. She believed herself to be in charge of her own life.

The weeks until the end of term slipped away with amazing rapidity. As a private school, Brentleigh closed its gates at the end of November and now Brooke had time to spend with Lucia. In the past month, Paul had been interstate several times on business and Brooke sensed Carla wasn't spending as much time with her young cousin as she should. Carla was blooming, noticeably slimmer, with invitations everywhere, while the sixteen-year-old Lucia, too young to be involved in the social whirl and terrified of it, remained much the same, very shy and insecure.

In the very first week of the holidays Brooke rang Paul at his office and discovered that like everyone else she had to have an appointment to see him. Slightly piqued, she listened to the time his secretary gave her and hung up, frowning sightlessly at a painting on the wall. If she hadn't decided on properly outfitting Lucia she wouldn't have bothered, but Lucia's blossoming seemed most important.

The Corelli executive offices were most impressive, especially to anyone seeing them for the first time. Brooke had perched herself on the edge of a plush real leather sofa, her long slender legs drawn neatly to one side and crossed at the ankles. She looked the picture of cool elegance in a white linen safari-look suit with a sun-yellow silk shirt beneath, but inside she was feeling rather terrible. In trying to help Lucia wasn't she implying that there was considerable room for improvement? Perhaps Paul was blind to his daughter's superficial limitations, things that could be radically altered, like a new hairstyle for example. How would he take her interference? Far from being loverlike his manner with her had been extremely businesslike for the past weeks. Coming right down to it, he might have decided to call the deal of getting married right off. He wouldn't even have to give a reason.

Behind her desk, the good-looking young receptionist picked up the phone and breathed into it:

'Certainly, Mr Corelli!'

Brooke looked towards her and the girl smiled and nodded. 'Mr Corelli will see you now. Sorry to keep you waiting, but something is always happening around here.' She stood up and led Brooke across an ante-room, then down to Paul's office, cooing Brooke's name at the door, then closing it softly after her.

Paul stood up and moved across the room to her, taking her hand and just barely lifting it to his lips. 'It's so unlike you, Brooke, to think of visiting me.'

'I can hardly believe I'm here. I've been waiting fifteen minutes.'

'I'm sorry!' he smiled at her tart tone, and led her across the thickly carpeted floor, indicating that she take one of the black leather armchairs. On either side of the huge plate glass window behind his desk were major modern paintings by artists she recognised and another behind the sofa wall.

'I don't think I've ever seen such a stylish office!' she commented, trying to relax. As usual just facing him and those dark intent eyes made her fretful and vaguely excited.

'Thank you, Miss Howell. I don't think you came here to tell me that!' He moved with lithe grace and sat down in the armchair opposite her. 'What is it, little one, have you come to tell me you simply can't marry me?'

She lifted her head and met his mocking dark gaze. 'To be perfectly frank, I've come to talk about Lucia.'

'So?' He gave a characteristic Latin shrug.

'It's for you to consider, of course.'

'Tell me, *cara*,' he said rather pointedly. 'I was dying to talk about *us*, but I guess Lucia is of considerable interest.'

Brooke sighed and seemed to sink a little deeper into the armchair. 'You sound faintly hostile!'

'Not at all!' He leaned over and caught at her finger-tips. 'Perhaps a little disappointed. I don't wish to force you to marry me, but I think I've given you enough time.'

She shook her titian head almost mournfully. 'Please, Paul, may we talk about Lucia? I know you're a very busy man and I'd like to start right away.'

'Well, go ahead and start,' he invited sardonically. His black eyes slipped over her hair and her face, travelled over her slender frame and rested with amazing insolence on her exquisite young legs. 'What beautiful limbs you have!' he murmured, admiring them openly.

'How you exaggerate!' she said moodily, her green eyes beginning to flash storm signals.

'You have too many complexes, *cara mia*. I'm going to force you out of them. You're a beautiful woman, very desirable, yet you seem to find it alarming.'

'Yes,' she answered, and bit her full lower lip. 'With you, I do.'

'That's something at least!' He shifted further back in his armchair, looking indolent and full of a superb animal grace. 'About Lucia?'

Her red-gold hair made a thick silky halo about her face and her green eyes quickened with sympathetic interest. 'May I have your permission to take Lucia on a shopping spree? Unless you particularly like her long hair I'd like to get it restyled as well. With the summer and all the new activities we can plan on she'll be needing so many things, and her hair is weighing her little face down.' She kept looking at him, fearing she might offend him, but he seemed calmly meditative, his tilted-back head emphasising the deep cleft in his chin. 'What do you think?' Her hand fluttered rather helplessly and he caught it and this time carried it directly to his mouth.

'What a perfect little mother you'll make!'

Brooke muttered something incoherent, dismayed by the arrowhead of flame that was shooting from her palm, past the wrist and up her arm. 'Then it's all right?'

'Yes, darling,' he answered. 'Needless to say Papa is paying.'

He still held her hand and she withdrew it strongly, a delicate flush glowing under her skin. 'Good! I'll tell Lucia we have your blessing.'

'Only one thing!' he said suddenly, looking hard and businesslike. 'Can you not thank me?'

'Yes, of course. Thank you!' She stood up nervously and smoothed her linen skirt.

He too came to his feet, looking down at her creamy confused face with the heat of warm blood over the cheekbones. 'Lucia tells me she finds you very beautiful and kind. She admires you and I think she is prepared to love you, which means, I think, we should set the date of our wedding.'

'I'd hoped you'd forgotten all about it!'

'Don't be stupid, *piccola*,' he said coolly. 'I want a big church wedding so I can say to our grandchildren how beautiful a bride their grandmother made!' His hands closed over her shoulders and Brooke stood perfectly still beneath them, conscious of panic and a strange aching yearning.

'What was Lucia's mother's name?' she asked him. 'Where is she now?' There was a curious tightness in her usually pretty, low-keyed voice.

His hands hardened and his dark face was suddenly filled with shadows, almost remote. 'Her name was Lucia, like her daughter,' he answered finally. 'She was eighteen years old when she died and I have never ceased blaming myself. She trusted me and I would have married her, but she told no one. She went away and I waited. I would have brought her back had I known, but I did not until it was too late. The birth was premature and she died before I could get to her. She lived with an old couple who found out my name and sent for me. You can't imagine how I felt. Poor little Lucia! She thought I didn't love her. She knew somehow I would make my way in the world and she did not want to be a burden.'

'I'm so sorry,' Brooke said faintly. The chair was pressing against the back of her knees and she allowed him to put her gently back into it.

'Does Lucia know the story?'

'She knows I would have married her mother had she lived. This I swear. I had some reputation in the village as a Lothario, but no one doubted my honour. Lucia was a child, a little shadow that always followed me. She was always there wherever I turned, big eyes adoring. There was only one time, then nothing. I lost my head, but afterwards I worried. She was a good

girl, like my little Lucia, but very sensitive and shy—
someone who only lives through another person, the
man she loved. It was her tragedy that she chose to love
me.'

'She must have been brave even when she was completely desperate. Did she have no family?'

'She had no one who really cared!' he said harshly.
'So now you know Lucia's story. It is not very pleasant,
is it?'

'Your daughter still has you,' she answered quietly,
aware of the pain in him. Paul Corelli, the ruthless
tycoon, with his arrogant mocking face, was still hurt
badly by a youthful tragedy.

'For years afterwards when I thought of little Lucia
dying alone I nearly went out of my mind, but I held
to my daughter tightly. For her I have made my fortune. For the son I have yet to have. I've had many
women since, but no woman has ever again borne my
child. So help me God, I intend to marry you!' His
black eyes glittered like jet over her frightened face.
'You are no forsaken, half-starved child, you are a
woman of passion and spirit—or you could be when
you unfold. Give me your answer now, because I'm not
going to follow you around like a puppy dog. When
will you marry me?'

His eyes flashed so brightly Brooke almost exclaimed
in a panic. With anyone else trying to rush her into
such a decision she would have told them to go and
jump off the building, but it was unthinkable to say
such a thing to Paul Corelli. There was a violence in
him and a purpose that set up a swirling sea of excitement. He even seemed sick to death of her tardi-
ness as though another day of hesitation would fore-
close their deal.

Swept by his personality and his devastating impatience, she found herself reaching out to him almost pleadingly. 'Please, Paul!'

'Please *nothing*!' He almost hurtled her to her feet, holding her by both arms. 'How long will it take you to arrange things, a month, six weeks?'

She was shaking, yet his eyes were leaping over her as though she was perfectly steady. 'All of s-s-six weeks,' she stammered.

'So be it!' He let her go as swiftly as he had taken hold of her, and it broke Brooke's crushing tension.

'So that's off the agenda!' she said furiously. 'Corelli, buying up everything in sight—*me*, a house, a parcel of land!' Sparks of anger and bitterness seared her like a flame, bringing her creamy face to startling, vivid life. He was full of ambition and she was already tied up. A Corelli possession. She twisted violently away and went to reach for her handbag, but he pulled her into his arms with devastating suddenness, pressing her against his lithe body, pinning her arms behind her back.

'What makes you the way you are?' he asked tautly, 'or is there no rose without thorns? In the beginning you told me you disliked me intensely, yet now you are shocked and offended that I don't kiss you until you cry out!'

'I'm not another one of your women!' she cried recklessly, and her voice throbbed with a mad humiliation.

'You are *my* woman!' he gritted between clenched teeth, 'and the sooner you learn it the better!'

Everything seemed to swim before her eyes. The hunter advancing upon her. He lowered his dark head almost savagely and took her mouth, forcing it open, utterly ruthless, draining its sweetness until she moaned, almost shattered by the passion and the violence that was in him. Emotionally she was being swept outside all safety, yet he had shifted his cruel hold to encircle her slender body almost protectively, kissing her so deeply she was made hungry or thirsty for she didn't know what. Boldly his hands came up and cupped her young breasts, the warmth of his hands searing the silk arousing her so that she was taken by shock and abandon. She was clinging to him, her mouth moving over his skin, so scented of the male, everything happened so fast it was almost a matter for appalled wonder.

'Will you sleep with me when we're married?' he asked against her mouth. His fingers wound through the silky tendrils of her hair, caressed her nape, his voice very deep and tender, promising ecstasy, delight. It was so easy for him, and in spite of the urgent, almost helpless reponse of her body Brooke pulled back from him, forcing her head to clear.

'One thing at a time!' she said curtly, as though her pride only permitted her one course. 'You promised me when *I'm* ready!'

'And you're not?' He looked down at her steadily.

'Just think—you don't love me!' she cried tearfully. 'I don't love you. It's barbaric!'

Paul moved back and took a cigarette from the silver box on his desk. His strong lean hands were perfectly steady. 'And you wish we did?' he asked almost wearily.

'I told you once before it seems wrong to marry without love.'

'But you won't let me!' he said as though she intrigued him. 'I have only ever wanted one woman, not six dozen as you seem to think. Let me look after you as if you were just a little girl. I promise I will be so good to you, you won't deny me anything.'

'Do I have your word?' she asked compulsively.

'So far and no further. So long as you don't deliberately tempt me your bed is inviolate until such time as you come to know yourself better.'

'Then I must believe you!' she said intensely.

'Of course.' He gave her a brief smile that was as cool as his eyes. 'Your mother will like to take care of things, I imagine. She will enjoy it, and I would like the reception to be held at Wintersweet.'

Colour flared in her cheeks and she bent down and retrieved her handbag. 'If there's anything else you decide please let me know!'

'Poor little one!' he drawled sardonically, his heavy-lidded eyes half closed against the thin veil of smoke. 'Anyway, I am very grateful to you for the interest you have taken in my daughter. She thinks we are very much in love. Please don't disillusion her.'

'And Carla?' Brooke retorted flashingly.

'Come,' he said, and his dark face assumed an expression of incredible hauteur, 'what has Carla to do with anything?'

'What did she do to forfeit *her* rights?' Brooke walked away, unafraid, to the door.

'A little jealousy won't hurt you!' he returned blandly. 'But how is one jealous where there is no feeling?'

Brooke swung about with silken grace, her golden-green eyes jewel-like in her flushed face. 'If it's all right with you I'll take care of Lucia today. Some of my girls from Brentleigh are staying home over the holidays, and I'd like Lucia to meet them when she's ready. She needs the company of girls of her own age. Later on we'll discuss what you intend to do about furthering her education. I can recommend Brentleigh. It has an excellent reputation.' She could feel the silken thickness of her hair about her face and she shook it back. 'I suppose I've lost all my lipstick, have I?'

He gazed at her for a long moment, then he laughed. 'Let us say you do not in the least look like a scotty schoolteacher!'

'Never mind, I'll fix it later!' Away from him her spirit and confidence was returned to her. '*Ciao!*' she said breezily, and went swiftly through the door.

The shopping expedition would have been a great success except for one thing: Carla insisted on going with them, her nonchalant, amused dark eyes seeming to destroy Lucia's frail confidence. Her sweet smile became less gay, her glance fluttering between Brooke and her mocking cousin, until finally Brooke determined she had to speak her mind. Lucia had looked charming in her last outfit, yet Carla had waved it away with such purpose that Lucia and the salesgirl both looked desolated. It didn't seem the moment for Brooke to intervene, but she did so immediately Lucia walked away to change into something else.

Carla was leaning back in her chair, her pretty legs crossed high, mocking laughter in her dark eyes. 'She is plain, the little one, *no*?'

'You shouldn't upset her,' Brooke said more heatedly than she intended. 'She could look charming given the chance.'

'So you say,' Carla drawled. 'Tell me, why do you do this? To please Paul?'

'To please *Lucia*!' Brooke returned firmly. 'I'm quite

fond of her and she has no weapons against anyone like you. You are her cousin, yet you seem to be going out of your way to destroy her confidence.'

'Nonsense, I'm only teasing!' said Carla, her dark eyes hard. 'Besides, she is not really my cousin, although there was a time I was nearly her stepmamma!'

'I think it's wonderful that a marriage didn't come about. I don't think you would have been very kind to Lucia. What I can't understand is how you came to accompany her out. She speaks very highly of her aunt and uncle and her little cousins, so they must have thought you would look out for her.'

'And I haven't?' Carla asked in that gay, insincere fashion. 'Paul asked me out, Miss Howell, and I think you've sensed I would do anything for Paul.' Her dark eyes glittered and her soft laugh was insinuating, triumphant. 'It's almost been like old times. Isn't that how you say it?'

'Then you must be rather unhappy that he intends to marry me,' Brooke met the scheming mind head on.

'The question is *when*?' Carla returned insolently. 'They tell me cold feet go with pale skin. You are not the woman for Paul. How could you hope to hold him? You, a prim little virgin! You could never hope to understand him or give back fire for fire. He is a real man and you would only ruin his life.'

'It doesn't appear that way to him,' Brooke said smoothly, though her heart was hammering inside.

Carla gave a little exclamation that Brooke didn't understand. 'It's not you he wants,' she said scornfully, 'it's the gracious way of life. This old house you have, so big and imposing. Paul has always had great plans. He was very poor as a child. He is what is called a self-made man, a millionaire many times over. He has learned much. Now he is the sophisticated man of the world able to buy anything he pleases but he has not forgotten his childhood. You have something to offer, that is true, and I think you know what it is!'

'Well, that rather settles it, doesn't it?' Brooke answered coolly. 'I'm quite happy with the bargain. Paul has something to offer me too!'

'Such as?' Carla asked with such venom that Brooke drew back instinctively as though confronted with a roused snake.

'None of your business,' Brooke said with no belligerence in her calm voice. 'Shall we call a truce? Lucia is returning and I won't permit you to upset her. Her father wouldn't like it.'

For an instant Carla went rigid, then she jumped to her feet. 'Excuse me,' she said grandly, 'I'm quite bored with this session. See you later, Lucia.' Her false smile flashed towards Lucia, hesitating at the entrance to the dressing rooms.

Lucia considered this gravely, her eyes seeking Brooke's, then she answered with surprising composure. 'Thank you for coming, Carla. Yes, I'll see you back at the apartment. Papa is taking us to the opera.'

After that, things went much better, though Brooke had a stunning mental picture of Carla in evening dress showing a delectable amount of bosom. One could scarcely follow Paul around, but wherever he was, there seemed to be a woman. She shuddered even remembering the last time she had seen him with Cathy Benton. Bees to the honey! It worked both ways, and it haunted her.

Lucia gave a small pirouette to display the full skirt of her dress. She and the salesgirl had chosen it together and now they were waiting for Brooke's opinion.

'Perfect!' Brooke surveyed the young girl from head to toe. 'You're really very graceful. Now, what about sports clothes? You can expect to go swimming and sailing and we have a tennis court at Wintersweet if you're interested. I'm considered quite a good player, so I could help you there, and I'd like to give a little party for you to meet some young friends your own age.'

Lucia's nervous smile betrayed her anxiety and Brooke smiled into her eyes. 'Don't you worry, I'll be there to help you. I promise you it won't be at all nerve-racking, but *fun*.' She turned her titian head and smiled at the salesgirl. 'You know the sort of thing I mean, young and trendy, shirts and shorts and skirts, colours co-ordinated so they'll all mix and match.'

The owner of the boutique came back towards them smiling brightly. 'Very charming!' Stepping back a little, she surveyed Lucia's slight figure. 'Only a very young girl could wear that. It suits you beautifully dear. By the way, Miss Howell,' she transferred her effusive gaze to Brooke, 'there's something that's just come in I'd like you to see. Too lovely—though I knew the minute I saw it, it would suit you.'

Brooke smiled and said she would look at it, knowing quite well she wouldn't be able to pay for it. Both Mamma and Louise had proved very profitable customers in the past, but Brooke was in the habit of budgeting and the words 'charge it' didn't fall easily from her lips. At least Lucia didn't have that problem, for Paul didn't care in the least how much they spent and the sleek, beautifully groomed owner of this very exclusive boutique was visibly awed by the prospect of dressing Paul Corelli's young daughter. No saleswoman worth her salt overlooked future good customers, even if Brooke found the obvious flattery a little irritating.

When it was all over and arrangements made for Lucia's new wardrobe to be sent they just had time for a quick cup of coffee and a sandwich before the rush to the hairdresser. Lucia kept on exclaiming, even as she was rushing by Brooke's side, that she was taking up too much of Brooke's time, but Brooke told her quite truthfully that she was enjoying herself.

Raymond took one look at Lucia's hair and cringed, throwing his hands theatrically into the air while Lucia sat in the chair staring at him with wide, frightened eyes. Brooke in the vacant chair beside her spoke out staunchly:

'The hair itself is good, glossy and luxuriant, you will work magic with it, Raymond, I know!'

For answer he rolled his eyes. 'The problem is to get rid of all *this*!' As he spoke he was removing the pins from Lucia's wealth of hair and it tumbled over her shoulders and down her back. 'Good hair, yes,' he said, 'the style more suitable for a matron of great majesty.'

'You've got the idea!' Brooke smiled encouragement at Lucia, whose frightened expression was beginning to clear. 'I'll take myself off for an hour and a half. You'll be very safe with Raymond. He's almost a member of the family.'

'Ah,' said Raymond, 'and how is your dear mother? The new style I gave her was very nice.'

Brooke acknowledged this very pleasantly and stood up. 'For Lucia I thought a mid-length, blow-waved back from her face.'

'Leave this to me, young lady!' Raymond said repressively, and Brooke smiled and quietly went away. If anyone could make Lucia look super it was Raymond. By the time she got back later on in the after-

CHAPTER SIX

Now she had committed herself to Paul, Brooke found it impossible to go back. Before she had sailed through her life with a few rough bits, but now it was like being out in a power boat with everything happening so fast there was no time to worry about anything. The pace was dazzling and she was assailed with invitations from every side. Every one wanted to meet her fiancé. They'd heard of him, of course, who hadn't? But now they wanted to meet him before they were invited to the wedding.

As her fiancé, Paul escorted her everywhere, but never once did he kiss her mouth, just a hand or a cheek, although he was always extremely courteous and mindful of appearances. Everyone thought it the romance of the year and Paul responded with an excellent characterisation of a man very deeply and happily in love. In public, that was. In private there was no hint of the lover in his attitude. Brooke and Lucia might have been interchangeable, so gently and benignly were they indulged.

Lillian was in her element, playing hostess with unlimited funds. There were parties and brunches all over Christmas and the holiday period, and the Ashton treasures were finding their way back into the house. By now, Paul had bought it and the wedding date was set for January the eleventh, Lillian's birthday. There was no way to turn back and everyone, with the disturbing exception of Carla, seemed delighted. Their engagement party at Christmas had been wonderful, with over three hundred guests and Wintersweet looking as it hadn't done since long before Grandfather had died. Even Maggie was slightly giddy working at Paul's pace, negotiating the transfer of certain antiques with the buying price made so attractive very few collectors turned it down. The restoration of the house and garden continued at a breathless rate, with workmen and gardeners all over the place and vans pulling up with all the missing pieces of furniture Maggie had found or bringing still more wedding presents to fill every available spare room.

There were hundreds of expensive gifts to bind Brooke more tightly than ever to her dynamic, enigmatic fiancé. The qualities that had made him a millionaire were being exhibited to the household every day and Brooke concluded that any other man would have been broken by ulcers. Yet somehow Paul continued to oversee all his various enterprises, run Maggie off her feet, escort Brooke everywhere, present himself at Wintersweet every day to check on the work done, and effortlessly charm Mamma and Louise.

A settlement had been reached between Mamma and Paul, but Brooke thought there was no point in asking about it. Her mother was warm and gay and smiling all the time, and she and Louise had had a wonderful time selecting Brooke's trousseau, plunging their pretty hands ecstatically into the mounting exquisite piles of lingerie and the fantastically beautiful night attire. Though she felt like it, Brooke didn't permit herself one sour smile. Paul was unlikely to see her in any of *that*!

The night before her wedding Brooke shut herself in her room and cried her eyes out. She would have continued with abandon, only Mamma stood outside the door, knocking and calling anxiously.

'Darling girl, let me in!'

For a moment Brooke considered feigning deafness, but she knew her mother wouldn't go away. She rolled off the bed, hastily wiped the tears from her green eyes and went to the door, throwing it open so her mother could come inside.

Lillian's blue eyes were full of motherly concern. 'Precious girl!' she said, staring up at her daughter, 'don't cry any more, you'll ruin your looks and you'll want to be your most beautiful for Paul!'

This seemed to make matters worse. Brooke gave a groan and collapsed on the bed, and Louise who had been hovering outside rushed into the bedroom. 'What is it, Mamma? What's wrong with her?'

'Just a little case of bridal jitters,' Lillian said soothingly. 'It happens all the time.'

Louise went over to her sister and patted her arm. 'It's going to be a lovely wedding, Brooke. Your dress is gorgeous and so is mine. Make sure when you throw your bouquet I get it!'

'Not to worry, darling!' Lillian smiled. 'You're going to dazzle them in London. I think we'll go there first. Travelling is heavenly if one stays at all the best places and I've promised Paul I'll visit his sister in Kenya. They have a beautiful property, I believe. I'm sure they wouldn't recognise little Lucia. We really have done wonders for the child. She looks almost pretty these days!'

'Brooke?' Louise asked tentatively. It was obvious Brooke wasn't listening to one word their mother was saying.

'It's all right, go to bed.' Brooke sat up and smoothed

her tumbled hair. 'I always cry when I'm in a particularly happy frame of mind.' Her hands were trembling,
but she hoped neither her mother nor Louise would
notice.

'Yes, we'll all go to bed!' Lillian agreed, and got to
her feet. 'God bless you, my darling.' She moved on
tiny feet over to her younger daughter to kiss Brooke's
cheek. 'I know I shall weep tomorrow. *Dearly beloved,
we are gathered together ...*'

'*Please*, Mamma!' Brooke cried so piteously that
Lillian broke off in amazement.

'You're tired, darling. It's been all too much for you.
Louise, go downstairs and get your sister some hot
milk.'

'Better still, a brandy!' said Brooke, and began to
laugh.

A long look passed between Louise and her mother.
'Very well, a brandy, then. Hurry along, Louise. My
little girl needs something to steady herself!'

'That's true enough, I'm nearly at breaking point!'

The light shone on Louise's pale hair. For a moment
she stood rigidly, her blue eyes fixed on her sister's face.
'You love him, don't you, Brooke?'

Her desolate expression thrust a knife in Brooke's
tender heart. 'Of course I do, darling. Are you sure I
haven't hurt *you*? After all, not so very long ago we
were planning on your wedding.'

Louise's eyes softened and she spoke in her gentle
voice. 'I'd be no match for Paul, but you are. I'm
not in the least jealous, you know that. He's wonderful
to turn to, but I think he might be very difficult to
live with. For me, at least,' she added hastily as her
mother frowned. 'Everyone is envying you like crazy.
Why do you think Cathy Benton went overseas? She

couldn't bear to be here with you landing the biggest catch of the year. Paul is so exciting, so glamorous, but I think I'll like him best as a brother-in-law!'

'And your mother, dear, is overjoyed!' Lillian said firmly. 'When you first told me Paul wanted to marry you I couldn't believe it, but now I see it will work perfectly, and you're so good with Lucia. Of course it's all your teaching experience, and you're older. I swear I'd love my future son-in-law if only because he has kept Wintersweet in the family. Young people should start their married life in their own home, and what could be more perfect than here? Really Grandfather would be very pleased!' Lillian's eyes grew misty and she seemed very pleased and happy. 'Now, darling, I'll say goodnight. It's going to be a great day in the morning!' She gave a little delighted laugh and slipped her arm around Louise's waist. 'Your turn is next, dear. Leave it to Mamma!'

Surprisingly Louise took this a little doubtfully; her blue eyes met her sister's and gave the faintest wink. 'I'll bring you up that little drop of brandy,' she promised, 'and I might have one myself. By the way, I never thought to tell you Patrick has asked me to marry him.'

'Poor Patrick!' said Lillian, and turned her daughter away. 'He's not nearly good enough for you.'

'You'd be surprised. He's changed!' Louise returned almost mockingly, and inside her bedroom Brooke overheard it and suddenly laughed. She hadn't had time to notice that Louise's own character had firmed over the past months.

St Martin's was packed. Patrick and Nigel acted as ushers, and found to their surprise that the groom had just as many guests as the bride. The occasion was formal and the time late afternoon, so the younger women guests wore flowers in their hair or ribbons and the smart matrons chic little bits of nothing. Lillian looked entrancingly youthful and pretty as the mother of the bride and at the altar the bridesmaids stood waiting like a bouquet of sweet peas, with Louise as chief bridesmaid in a heavy shade of blue chiffon, Emma and Jane Carnegie, close friends of both sisters since childhood, in lilac and rose and the youngest bridesmaid, Lucia, in a shade of pink vastly becoming to her colouring. The best man was the distinguished physician Dr Alessandro Bonetto and the groomsman Ross McClary, son and heir of George McClary the real estate tycoon.

At the rear of the church Brooke was trembling as if she was standing in an icy gust of wind. She looked very pale, very vulnerable, and most certainly more beautiful than she had ever looked in her life. Her dress was exquisitely fashioned of heavy magnolia satin and on her beautiful titian hair she wore a mantilla of Brussels lace that looked wonderful and drew little murmurs of surprised delight. Her bouquet was all white except for the green touches of foliage and it served to hide her shaking hands, but then it was time to move down the aisle towards the man who was waiting for her, and her godfather, Sir Anthony Carnegie, later remarked that he thought her so nervous he doubted whether they would make it.

The ceremony passed like a dream. Brooke seemed scarcely aware of anything except the dark stranger by her side. The only thing that sustained her was the thought that although he was now her husband she didn't have to sleep with him. Not yet! She was really overcome by the solemnity of what she had just done, the awesomeness of committing herself body and soul to this man called Paul Corelli.

Afterwards at Wintersweet they stood side by side receiving congratulations like Royalty with a public face, while inside Brooke was absolutely numb. Her face was faintly flushed with colour, her mouth glowed softly and her eyes were as brilliant as jewels. Paul had not kissed her at the end of the ceremony, though he had returned his vows with vibrant fervency to her hushed whisper. It seemed like a mercy they were now assailed by family and guests.

Bemused and shaken, Brooke went through the next few hours in a trance. A few times she had caught Carla staring at her with peculiar intensity, but nothing really registered except the unfathomable depths of Paul's eyes and the deep caressing timbre of his voice. If his accent seemed more pronounced she didn't notice, only searching in vain for a waiting look in his dark eyes. Paul Corelli, the hunger, the sleeping tiger. Hadn't she always called him that?

When she was left alone for a few seconds Carla surged up to her, showing far too much bosom for a wedding, her dark gaze fixed and feverish. 'Congratulations, *cara*,' she drawled softly. 'You have no ordinary man, you know that? I can tell you, I know that. He was mine before yours!'

'I don't believe it!' Brooke retorted as though she had an absolute belief in her new husband's integrity.

Carla seemed taken aback. 'Why don't you ask him?' she flared back, sounding goaded.

'No need!' Brooke actually smiled for the benefit of the interested stares. 'Please excuse me, Carla, Lucia is trying to attract my attention.'

Lucia, in fact, was doing just that, determined to

guard Brooke against Carla's strange jealousy, for unwisely Carla had given herself away on many occasions.

'Is everything all right, Brooke?' she asked urgently. 'Please do not take any notice of anything Carla might say. I think she has had a little too much to drink. Even I have had a glass of champagne!'

Before Brooke could answer Paul was by her side, so dark and handsome, so impeccably turned out she audibly caught her breath.

'It's time for us to leave, darling!'

There was no trace of sardonic mockery in his voice, yet the colour rushed to her cheeks and she refused to meet his eyes. Lucia threw herself at her father and he gathered her to him, kissing her tenderly, murmuring to her in their own language. After a moment Lucia drew back, her small face radiant, then shyly and very sweetly she saluted Brooke's satiny cheek. 'I am profoundly happy that we are now one family!'

She spoke with such obvious love and sincerity that the quick emotional tears glittered in Brooke's sparkling eyes. 'Thank you, darling!'

It was about ten o'clock, but the guests were still enjoying themselves immensely, wandering through the beautiful rooms and the floodlit garden, some still going back and forth to the buffets, others drinking the champagne that so enhanced such occasions, all of them convinced they had witnessed an unbearably lovely ceremony. The groom was a dream and the bride couldn't have looked more beautiful.

Paul had insisted it was necessary to take a short honeymoon of sorts and it had been agreed they would go back to the penthouse for that one night, then they were due to fly to San Francisco in the morning. Paul's commitments at that time only allowed a short week for being out of the country. Later on they would take a world trip. It never occurred to anyone to disbelieve a word of it.

The good wishes and congratulations continued to pour over them right until the minute they pulled out of the drive. No one dared tie anything to the Lamborghini's bumper bar and the last thing Brooke saw was her sister's face, beautiful with love and pleasure. Patrick was beside her and Louise *had* caught her bouquet. Brooke tilted her head back, drooping a little in the seat.

'It's all over,' her husband said quietly.

'No, it's begun!' she answered, faintly hysterically.

'Calm yourself, darling,' he said sombrely. 'We are man and wife and I feel it deeply, but I have promised you I will respect your wishes.'

She coloured, then paled and stared out the window at the familiar flying miles. 'What time do we leave in the morning?'

'Not early, noon.' He turned his head and glanced at her for a few seconds. 'You look like a swan. I was very, very proud of you.'

Her skin gleamed like a pearl in the faint light and she was moved by some kind of passion in his voice. If he touched her or spoke to her again in that deep caressing voice she would burst into a storm of weeping, an agony of knowing herself wanted but not loved. He had great power over her and she knew in her heart he could break her. She shut her eyes quickly and passionately, and when she opened them again they were back at Paul's penthouse.

Her heart began to beat with a new rapidity, but he appeared even more self-assured than ever. 'Come, little one, before you pass out on me.'

She hesitated for a moment, then she gave him her hand and he drew her out of the car, holding her still for a moment and looking down at her shining beauty. Her green eyes were incandescent, very wary and feminine.

'Please let's go up. I feel strange in this dress.'

'Really?' One winged black eyebrow shot up. 'I love it. Were it not for your eyes and your woman's mouth you would look celestial. Tell me, why did you not change?'

'There didn't seem much point!' There was a hard lump of excitement in her throat, an anguish of forbidden desire, and he was a very sensual man. She feared him, but most of all she feared herself. The little excited pinpoints of gold in her eyes were both provocative and dangerous.

Inside the apartment it was very hushed. 'Is Gianni coming back?' she asked foolishly.

Paul's low laugh was mocking. 'Please, *bambina*! You would shock him out of his mind with such a question. He believes us to be deeply in love.' He flicked a switch and the apartment was bathed in soft lights, visually very tranquil, yet exotic. The paintings and the gleaming collection of Tibetan gilt bronzes were spotlit, the golden figures of gods and goddesses and Buddhas floating in vibrant pools of light.

Brooke turned her glowing head and looked back at Paul, the colour flaring under her skin. His physical hold on her was shaming, yet she admired his brilliant mind. He looked very masculine, sophisticated, yet openly sensuous. A chain of bizarre images unfolded in her mind and she moved lightly and swiftly across the room as if to escape her own imagination, staring out at the dazzling diamond lights of the city by night.

She felt tears prick her eyes, but she didn't care. She was a married woman and instead of being rapturously happy she was lost in a bitter-sweet torment. There could be no easy relationship with Paul. His nature and temperament would demand total involvement.

'What is it, little one?'

He spoke with kindness and understanding, but she knew if he touched her she would burst into flame.

'Nothing, I'm a little tired!' He had come to join her, staring out over the fairy lights, his profile, except for the faint hump at the bridge of his nose, that of a beautiful classical statue. But statues didn't have black eyes that sparkled and voices that could melt stone. Her face must be very easy to read, the panic and be-wilderment.

'You aren't afraid of me, are you?' he asked suddenly.

'How could I be?' Brooke said helplessly. 'You're my husband. I trust you.'

'Then turn to me, *mia cara*!'

She closed her eyes and felt his strong hands on her shoulders. 'What are you nerving yourself for?' he asked a little curtly. 'Do you expect me to ravish you like the barbarian you once called me?'

'No, Paul,' she said softly.

'Then open your eyes.'

She did so and saw the sparkle had melted to black velvet. She had always considered herself a very modern young woman, but she could see now that she was very young and inexperienced. There was a big gap between them in temperament and behaviour and she was as ignorant of unleashed emotion as Paul was master of it. She was trembling under his hands, but she tried to keep her gaze steady, her golden-green eyes enormous in her overwrought face.

He touched a finger to her quivering mouth and smiled. 'I have a present for my wife,' he said gently. 'It has been an exalted day for me, little one. Do not spoil it. In a moment you may sleep. My room is yours and I will use the guestroom.'

There were tears in her eyes and quickly she blinked them away. 'I have something for you too, but I'm afraid I've forgotten it. Everything seemed to go out of my head.'

'No matter!' he said lightly. 'Naturally I expect you to give it to me again. I shall treasure it.'

'But you don't even know what it is!'

'*You* are giving it to me, aren't you?' he said meaningfully.

Brooke moved to the centre of the room while he walked away to a wall safe concealed behind a large abstract painting. It was so quiet in the room she could hear the wild beat of her heart. The magnolia satin of her wedding dress was gleaming in the light and she touched it in wonderment, scarcely able to comprehend the events of the day. Paul was walking back to her holding a large flat black velvet box. 'These bear the superb name of Cartier. I wanted nothing *ordinary* for you!'

In front of her dazzled eyes he opened the box and took a necklace and matching earrings into his hand, allowing the light to catch the stones in all their brilliance, diamonds and emeralds set in yellow gold and platinum. 'Beautiful, aren't they?' he murmured, because she seemed to be hypnotised by the glitter.

Her trembling was something she couldn't control and it was increasing. She said, without thinking, 'I could never wear that!'

'On the contrary, you are going to wear it now.

Allow me that, my love!' His voice deepened sardonically. 'I have never seen such a jittery bride when heaven
knows you've insisted on a platonic holiday. Turn
around, my child, and afterwards you can go to bed.'

His warm fingers touched her nape and he drew her
backwards towards the mirror above the gilded con-
sole table in the entrance hall. There was a tingling
sensation all over her body. She had never dreamed
anyone could move her like this man did. This man,
her husband, though their marriage had no true
meaning.

'It's too beautiful for words!' she said huskily, A
small rope of diamonds encircled her neck with a large
emerald at her breast representing a flower's heart
clustered around with diamonds and an encircling
spray of smaller emeralds for leaves. The craftsmanship
was superb, the beauty and elegance held in a tasteful
restraint.

'You'll have to have your ears pierced for the earrings,' Paul said casually, though his eyes were moving
with a peculiar intensity over the petal smoothness of
her face and throat. 'We can have that done in 'Frisco.
It's one of the world's most beautiful cities. You will
love it, and I'll take you everywhere, including the
Latin Quarter at North Beach. It's quite a famous
entertainment area and I have a brother who lives
there. Most of the people who live there are of Italian
descent, but no gangsters, I promise you. Once I
thought to live there, but I love Sydney too. The two
cities have much in common, the natural beauty and
excitement. There is something always happening.'

Brooke knew he was talking casually to lift her mood,
but she couldn't respond. There were so many things
she didn't know about him, so many things she hadn't

even asked. He had really lived his life while she had lived in sheltered protection, cushioned from all the hard knocks in life. Slowly and carefully she turned in his arms, like a little girl being her most obedient and polite. 'Thank you!' she said to this dashing, very romantic figure who was her husband.

'Can you not do better than that?' There was a faint challenge in the set of his head, the relaxed grace of his lean, hard body.

'Not right now,' she said softly. 'This is new to me, Paul. You must realise and be patient!'

'*Madre mia!*' he struck a hand to his head. 'Such patience is not in character. Surely you're not going to ask me to wait a hundred years?'

'We've agreed all along!'

'That's true!' he said flatly for such a musical voice. 'I don't want you afterwards calling me names. One chaste kiss from my bride and I am fully prepared to have a cold shower!' His black eyes sparkled over her. 'Come and see for yourself if you don't believe it.'

He could see the tears in her eyes and his imperious dark face seemed to tighten and sharpen. 'All right, little one, I struggle with my conscience and it wins. You see,' he added, and raised her hand to his mouth, pressing a real kiss on the tips of her fingers, then the palm, 'for you, I am determined to reshape myself, but I am a weak man, and curiously I won't be able to sleep unless you kiss me.' His expression changed to one of sharp humour and dutifully Brooke lifted her face, her green and gold eyes slowly closing.

The first touch of his mouth was a ravishment, his mouth moving over hers as though he loved the shape and taste of it. She could feel her knees give way and he gathered her into him, hungrily, tenderly, his hand encircling and caressing her throat, lifting the chain of diamonds over his fingers. He was murmuring to her in his own language and it was incredibly seductive, a drug she could easily become addicted to. She shook her titian head a little to right the mistily dissolving world, fighting the breathless impulse to surrender to his sexual radiance. Every movement, every caress was deeply, gracefully erotic and she was clinging to him because she could not stand.

'Please, Paul!' she murmured with her last strength.

'Darling?' He lifted his head and his voice sounded a little dazed.

'I want to go to bed.'

'For God's sake, so do I!' He didn't speak violently, but somehow unsteadily. 'All right, little one, once you make up your mind, you make up your mind!'

Now he was releasing her she couldn't move, and he looked down at her creamy face and her trembling uncertainty and lifted her high in his arms. 'You can undress yourself, I hope? I do not mean you to leave me, otherwise I would offer. I would love to kiss every inch of your body, but I see it is not permitted, and God forbid I should rape my own wife.'

In his bedroom he lowered her very gently to the bed. 'Tell me you don't mean it?'

He was really very beautiful, she thought. In a way she had already begun to love him. There was something very thrilling about the bones and planes of his face, his dark colouring, the crooning melodic line of his voice. 'Goodnight, Paul,' she said softly, and as she did so she smiled, a lovely confidence coming back into her eyes.

'*Buona notte*, Signora Corelli!' he responded drily. 'If you hear a few cries during the night you'll know

I'm having nightmares. Do not get up to me. I might misunderstand.'

The week in San Francisco was perfect. It was cold, but it didn't seem to matter. Paul bought her a beautiful fur coat and high boots and they went everywhere, filling the days with sightseeing, riding the gaily clanging cable cars, shopping in the fabulous stores, standing on Mount Tamalpais looking down at the skyscrapers and the glistening white buildings clustered on the hills. At the famous Fisherman's Wharf they ate seafood and bought souvenirs and they toured Chinatown and all the museums and art galleries and visited a friend of Paul's at Sausalito, the artists' colony, north of the city and across the Golden Gate Bridge. Light snow fell all the time they were there, but it was far from unpleasant, almost romantic, cushioning them in an exciting, unreal world.

The night before they were due to fly home, Paul's older brother Marco gave a private party for them at one of the chain of restaurants he owned in the Latin Quarter, and by the time they arrived the place was alive with people enjoying themselves and wanting to meet them. Paul didn't in the least resemble his brother, except for one thing; they were both of them dynamic personalities with unquenchable energy and a inbuilt capacity for making money.

'Bella, bella, bella!' Marco gathered Brooke to him in a bear hug. He lacked Paul's height and uncanny elegance, but he was broad-shouldered and confident of his own attractiveness to women. He had been married twice, and twice divorced, and he had a beautiful blonde girl-friend in attendance.

There was much shouting and shoulder-clapping and

everyone lapsed into Italian as they always did when
they were moved. Paul and his success in his new
country was well known to them and it was gratifyingly
obvious that they had given instant approval to his new
bride. Brooke found herself fêted and set at a long table
with Marco as their host at its head. Then the feast
began.

It seemed to Brooke later that she had never eaten
such food, or drunk so much wine. It flowed as freely as
the laughter and the stories, and afterwards there was
dancing.

'Darling!' Paul's whisper was barely audible. He
held her closely, lovingly, as though they were on their
own.

'I don't think I've ever drunk so much *vino*!' she
said humorously, lifting her face to him. She was laughing and her green eyes were sparkling, her hair a flam-
ing cloud about her softly tinted face. 'Marco is being
too good to us!'

'He is overcome by your beauty, but you belong
to *me*.'

Without conscious volition her slender fingers moved
up to caress the smooth skin at the nape of his neck.
He had a beautifully shaped head and his hair curled
crisply. It was a heady, insistent feeling, the first such
movement she had ever made towards him, yet his
whole body tensed as if a whip had flicked his bare
skin.

'Do not play games with me, *cara*!'

'I'm sorry!' She moved her hand as though his skin
burned her.

'In another half hour we will go back to the hotel,'
he said tersely.

'But I thought you were enjoying yourself. *I* am!'

Perversely she wanted to hurt him after a week of pleasure and excessive indulgence. 'Your friend Dino asked me to dance with him and I haven't, when I promised.'

'And you want to?' he asked with his black eyes on her.

'Yes, very much!' she lied. 'Italians are beautiful natural dancers.'

'Don't enjoy it too much!' he warned her with only the faintest edge of humour.

When the music ended, a very pretty fair girl grabbed Paul's arm and nodded pleasantly to Brooke. 'Hi, may I borrow your husband?'

'There's a time limit!' Brooke smiled, equally pleasantly, and as the girl slid her arm through Paul's, his friend Dino quickly noticed and surged to Brooke's side, asking very politely and rather formally could he claim his dance now.

In an uncharacteristic spirit of abandon and feeling the frustrations of her relationship with Paul, Brooke went gracefully into the young man's arms. He was the same height as she was in high heels and he gazed soulfully into her eyes and after a moment began to croon softly near her ear. He was good and it was a love song she particularly liked. 'Is there an Italian who can't sing?' she asked provocatively.

'I'm sure there must be!' he said, smiling. 'Paul is a very lucky man to have found himself such a beautiful bride.'

She opened her green eyes wide. 'Don't I look starry-eyed?'

'You do!' he agreed fervently. 'I remember Paul had a passion for red hair.'

'Really? Perhaps you'd better tell me more.'

'Titian! I mean, *Titian*,' Dino said a little helplessly. 'You know, the great artist, Tiziano Vecellio. Paul too greatly admires that colouring as one admires a masterpiece.'

'Oh, I *see*!' said Brooke, smiling at Dino's faint discomfiture. Then the smile was wiped off her face, for over Dino's shoulder she saw her husband fractionally lifting one eyebrow to something the petite blonde had said to him. There was a slight edge to his smile, the light was on the glossy sheen of his hair and he looked quite something to look at. A shiver, partly ice, partly fire, went through her veins. She didn't *want* him to look at another woman like that. She didn't like it, and unfamiliar jealousy took her in its grip.

Dino was now crooning again, so she didn't have to make conversation. Paul hadn't once looked in their direction, and in some strange way all her bright pleasure in the evening was fading. The girl was very attractive and Paul seemed to have a fatal weakness for any colour hair. Hastily, so no one could possibly guess her thoughts, she began to ask Dino all about himself, without actually listening, and Dino, entranced, refused to surrender her for quite a long while.

Foolishly she had yielded to an impulse and she was even relieved when Paul came to claim her. 'Will you excuse me, Dino?' he asked dryly.

Dino drew in his breath and smiled. 'Why, certainly, *amica*. I am enchanted with your so beautiful wife.'

'Well, thank you for looking after her!' The tone was silky, yet Dino melted quickly away.

'Time to go home, *cara*,' said Paul with the merest lick of anger in his voice.

'I don't flatter myself you're jealous!' she retorted,

her own feelings transmuted to a quick, rising fever.

'Come now,' he returned with deceptive gentleness, 'who is there to be jealous of? Who would appeal to you, with hair a mass of flames and a heart of ice?'

She thrust back against his imprisoning hand. 'Marco is looking towards us, please don't let's quarrel.'

'No, it might work against you!' He linked his lean fingers through hers and they walked hand in hand through the crowd and over to where Marco was standing near the bar.

His white teeth flashed and he embraced Brooke first, then his brother. 'Next time you bring the little Lucia, understand? It is only a flight away, send her over for a holiday. Thank you for giving me this opportunity to meet my new sister. She is irresistible and I think a good match for you!'

Brooke smiled and thanked him again for giving them such a wonderful party, then Paul's arm was coiled about her and he was lifting his hand in salute to all his friends in the crowded room. All Brooke could do was continue to smile, crushed against her tall, dark husband, her green eyes huge and excited, the silken backward sweep of her hair falling back from her flushed face. They looked the perfect newly married couple. She *knew* they did, and all the time the suppressed fury and frustration of her loveless marriage was mounting within her.

On the way back to the hotel, she started an argument; she didn't know why she did, but she did. Ordinarily she never drank more than two glasses of wine, so perhaps it was that. Her heart seemed to be beating to suffocation, and she needed so much more from her husband. But what? He had been kindness and gallantry itself, so tender and indulgent he had often astonished her. So why now did she sound like a spoilt, unreasonable child? Paul sat aloof from her, leaving her to her low-pitched monologue, though he grasped her wrist firmly when they got out of the cab and marched her through the hotel foyer into the waiting elevator. It was a famous hotel and their suite had delighted her, but tonight she noticed none of it.

In a self-induced fury she swept into her bedroom, but she had good sense enough not to slam the door in her husband's face. If eyes were a guide to temperament, such an action might bring instant reprisal. There was great pride in Paul, a high-mettled masculinity that didn't go with being dominated, much less humiliated by a woman. Her ridiculous marriage was getting to her. For a whole week, she had been a sweet, happy person, now she was cracked. Nothing made sense, least of all herself.

Her fur slid down her arms and she threw it on the chair, reaching for the zip on her dress. It wouldn't come and she could have screamed aloud in frustration. It had cost the earth and the zipper wouldn't *work*!

'Why not let me do that?' Paul asked, lounging nonchalantly in the doorway. He had a drink in his hand and he looked very dark and fascinating. Brooke saw too he had taken off his jacket and tie.

'Thank you, don't bother!' she answered automatically, and started pulling at the zipper again.

'You'll tear it' he warned her, and put down his drink.

Brooke's flushed oval face was startled. Often she had dreamed about him coming towards her with just such a look on his face. 'Don't, Paul!' she said with a little thrill of anxiety.

'Oh, stop it, you ridiculous child!' He turned her a little forcefully, and after a moment of gentle persuasion slid the long zipper down the back of her dress.

'Thank you, you're very kind.' She didn't mean it, of course, and her green eyes told him so.

'Aren't you going to take it off?'

'I will when you go.'

His black eyes sparkled over her. 'You're dreadfully shy, aren't you? Why are you always bothering to hide yourself from me? I know what a woman looks like.'

A kind of madness seized her and his dark face went hazy. 'That's your big trouble!' she said bitterly, and stepped out of her beautiful velvet dress, standing willowy and slender in her long silky crêpe petticoat rimmed top and bottom with beige lace.

'Don't say things like that!' Paul warned in a voice that might have stopped her.

'Why not?' She whirled on him defiantly, her hair a fiery aureole about her vivid face.

'Because it's not true and I don't like it. Are you going to hold it against me for ever that I fathered an illegitimate child? I didn't love Lucia, but she loved me. What is this *illegitimate* anyway? Just a cruel easy word for you to use against me.'

She could feel her body trembling. His face in the overlight was pagan-like, harsh with contempt for her. 'Go to bed, you stupid little girl, I don't want to lay a hand on you.'

'And I'm glad!' Her need to hurt him as he hurt her was primitive, beyond her control. 'I couldn't bear you to touch me.'

'I know!' He looked full at her, his brilliant gaze hard and unwavering. 'Don't worry about it, I didn't marry you for your love!'

The shock of it hit her like a blow. She gave a little inarticulate moan, then she slid to the floor.

When she opened her eyes again she was resting quietly in Paul's arms.

'What happened?' he asked in a taut, subdued voice.

'I don't know!' her dazed green eyes swept his face. 'I don't feel ill or anything.'

'You gave me a bad fright!' He lifted her in his arms and laid her down on the bed. 'I admit I wanted to hurt you—I'm sorry.'

'I'm sorry, too,' she offered gravely, still clinging to his hand. 'We've had such a lovely week, I can't think why I was so argumentative!'

'It doesn't matter,' he said quietly. 'Perhaps we've been overdoing it. I've rushed you everywhere, and I must confess you look very fragile.'

'I've loved it!' she said, and immediately a shadow crossed her face. 'Don't be angry with me, Paul. I don't hold Lucia's little ghost against you. How could I? I love your daughter already. She's incredibly sweet in a way few people are. I want to help her and protect her and see that life for her is good.' She was holding his hand against her, feeling weak and floating.

'Where is your nightgown?' he asked her.

'Hanging in the wardrobe.'

'Then I'll get it for you.' He moved away from her abruptly.

'It's all right.' She tried to sit up. 'I have to wash my face and brush my teeth.'

'I'll leave you, then.' He came back to her with the exquisite long nightgown Mamma had picked out for her so lovingly. 'Goodnight.' He lifted her face and brushed her cheek with his mouth.

'Goodnight, Paul,' she whispered, a little frightened

by the remoteness of his manner. 'You're not angry with me?'

'Not with *you*!' His eyes travelled over her and though they were fathomless, unreflective of his thoughts, she gave a convulsive little shiver.

Stupid, ridiculous, girl! she thought. I've angered you, for all your unreadable expression. Her behaviour had been immature, triggered by the sight of another woman in his arms, the special way he had smiled. Whether she would admit it to herself or not, wasn't her infinite insecurity the root of her troubles? A honeymoon was a time for passion as well as tenderness. Paul had shown her a beautiful city. He had indulged her every wish and had proved himself a superb companion. But never once could she have accused him of trying to seduce her with sheer masculine beauty.

'If you need me, call out,' he said to her at the door, then he was gone, leaving her to her strange despair. Her whole body had become piercingly alive, yet she was tired ... tired ... tired.

As often happens after a night of upset and excitement Brooke fell into a deep, uneasy sleep. She couldn't admit to herself that she would have been comforted by the presence of her husband, neither could she forget he had told her plainly he hadn't married her for her love. At first her dreams were fragmentary, a weird kaleidoscope of people and places, then as she went deeper into the silent world of sleep she was back in her car heading straight for the deep blue water of the marina. She could see it all clearly. It was happening again, just as vividly. She drew in her breath sharply, jerking her body uncontrollably. All the doors of the car were locked except for the one on her side, yet she couldn't get out. Her shrill cry of terror still hung in the air as she fought out of her nightmare. Both her arms were stretched above her head and her heart was pounding so much she moved one hand down with an effort and covered her agitated breast.

A light went on in the adjoining room, then Paul was towering in the doorway staring in at the trembling figure in the bed. 'What in God's name is wrong?'

Her ragged little whisper betrayed her. 'I had a nightmare.'

He moved into her room and flicked the switch that lit the dressing table and the lamps at either side of the bed. His dark curls were faintly tousled and he wore a dark red robe with the navy collar of his pyjama jacket standing up rakishly round his throat.

'I'm sorry, did I wake you?'

'I wasn't sleeping!' he answered with faint asperity.

'What time is it?' She put her hands to her temples.

'The usual time you seem to wake up. It's after three.'

Her hair on the pillows glittered red-gold and her eyes were enormous and frightened. Paul came to her then and sat down on the side of the bed. 'What were you dreaming about?'

'Oh, going into the marina that day!' She flung out her hand poignantly and he caught it, lending her some of his abundant strength. Her eyes were shining with tears and her mouth trembling.

'*Don't!*' he said urgently.

His voice stopped her and the taut wariness of his expression. 'Surely you don't think I'm trying to tempt you to my bed?'

'If you're not, then you're playing with fire.'

'I couldn't be so shameless!' she said, and her cheeks flamed.

'With your own husband?' he countered smoothly. 'Do you want me to go, or I'll stay. Probably we'll both go to sleep straight away. Besides, it will look better in the morning if we use both beds.'

'All right!' Her eyes clung to his as though hypnotised.

His little mocking smile seemed to fade all at once. 'Little hypocrite!' he said tautly. 'You deny me, yet you want me.'

'Well, take me, then!' she cried in despair.

'Hush!' He lifted her then, right into his arms, while the room spun around them, turning her in his arms so she relaxed against his shoulder. 'No, little one, some day very soon, I will. I could arouse you very quickly, the ardent woman in you, but not like this, when you're frightened and overwrought.' He moved one hand along her smooth cheek. 'You're so beautiful ... so desirable, but first you have to learn how to love!'

'You might try to remember you don't love *me*!' she muttered, burrowing her head against his hard chest, inexpressibly comforted by his hard strong arms pressing her closer against him.

'Don't I?' he asked dryly. 'What a child you are!' He laid her back on the pillows and slipped his arms from under her. 'Some day you're going to tell me what I want to hear. It is only for that that I exercise this iron control. Maybe too to convince you I am quite different from what you believe.'

'Kiss me goodnight!' she said sleepily, her eyelids falling.

'If I do I'll probably stay awake for the rest of the night!' He cupped her face in his hands, lowering his head and kissing her so briefly she made a little moan of protest. Exhaustion was making everything melt away, the whirlwind of emotions that had left her spent.

For a moment Paul stood there looking at her, then he moved to the other bed and turned down the covers. '*Women!*' he murmured, and shook his head. 'I do not want you, *cara mia*, as a sacrifice!'

CHAPTER SEVEN

DURING the next few weeks Brooke noticed a marked change in herself, almost as if a new Brooke had emerged. Although she didn't laugh and talk as freely as she once had done she had never looked better. The summer sun had given her the lightest golden tan, and Paul spent so much money on her she had to upbraid him for his extravagance. Mamma and Louise had gone off on their travels and though she missed them she had Lucia for company, and she was very proud of being Mrs Paul Corelli and mistress of Wintersweet.

They did a lot of entertaining. It was expected, but Brooke didn't have to cope alone. They had a house-keeper, plus Gianni and a gardener who came in three times a week. In many ways it even seemed Paul relied on her, though she was never certain what time he would leave in the morning or what time he would arrive home at night. Big business, she came to find, was very demanding of one's time and she told herself it was enough to see little Lucia emerging shyly from her cocoon and Paul visibly pleased with her as his young, enchanting wife. At parties and dinners she continued to see other women looking at him with unmistakable expressions, but she just told herself quietly: He is *my* husband and he wants nothing sordid to touch our lives. It was like a dream somehow, yet it was real and it couldn't go on.

From her bedroom window Brooke saw Carla drive

up to the house, and bit her lip in slight agitation. She could never like Carla, though Carla's behaviour since they had arrived home had been quite pleasant and correct. She had decided not to return to Kenya immediately but to spend perhaps a year in a city she found fascinating—or she said it was the city. Brooke had the dismal notion that she really meant Paul. He had been very good to her, allowing her to keep on the apartment, and by this time they were meeting her at all the parties and functions they were invited to, and as she was a relative of Paul and Lucia it was necessary to invite her to their home.

This morning she wasn't invited, but she arrived all the same. Hastily Brooke smoothed her hair and went downstairs, arriving in the entrance hall just as Carla was moving in out of the sunlight.

'*Buon giorno!*' she called out like a challenge.

'How are you, Carla? How nice to see you.'

'Cut it out, *cara*,' Carla said crudely. 'I know and you know we do not like each other!'

'Then why have you come?' Brooke asked her crisply.

Carla lifted her drooping, heavy lids. 'Why, to return Paul's lighter, of course. He will be too busy to come back to the apartment, and anyone can see it's valuable.'

Lucia had been running down the stairs and when she saw Carla she stopped awkwardly. 'Oh, Carla,' she said, and looked quickly at Brooke.

'How are you, little one?' Carla asked mockingly. 'Come on down. I won't bite you.'

'Would you care for a cup of coffee?' Brooke asked abruptly. 'Lucia and I were just about to have one.'

'Lovely!' said Carla, her dark eyes darting all over the pictures and furniture. 'My, oh, my haven't there been some changes in this house since we first arrived?'

'Yes, Paul is very good to me.' Brooke fought to give an easy answer, though she felt sick and shaken inside. Carla was a voluptuous woman, every temptress she could think of rolled into one, and she had made no secret of her feeling for Paul. Brooke was certain Paul felt no love for Carla, but today, just looking at her, Brooke could see she could easily incite desire, and sometimes desire had to be assuaged, specially when a passionate man was bound to a woman who didn't allow him into her bed.

'Shall I tell Harry?' Lucia said to Brooke, almost shrinking from her soulless cousin.

'Yes, dear!' Brooke smiled at her. 'We'll have it on the terrace, I think. It's so much cooler there.'

Lucia nodded and made off towards the kitchen to give Harriet the order, and Brooke glanced across at Carla. 'If you'd like to come through. Perhaps you could give me the lighter now.'

'Why, certainly!' Carla opened her handbag and began to rummage through it. 'Oh, here it is. I didn't like to hold on to it. It would have made me feel too responsible.'

'I see,' Brooke said calmly. She knew before Carla put the lighter into her hand that it was the one she had given to Paul. 'You're quite right, it's eighteen-carat gold.' She stared at the lighter for a minute, then slipped it in her pocket, apparently treating the matter very lightly.

'Don't be angry,' Carla drawled. 'You're a very sweet, pure girl and you're legally married to Paul, but you must realise you can't satisfy him—or don't you even try?'

She was looking at Brooke with such sharp, malicious perception that Brooke felt the colour drain from her face. 'Are you trying to tell me Paul visits *you*?'

'Of course, I'm his lady!'

'I can't believe it!' Brooke returned cuttingly. 'He has much better taste.'

'You mean you don't *want* to believe it!' Carla said with hard and bitter irony. 'Yours isn't the usual marriage, is it?'

The colour had completely left Brooke's high cheekbones. 'What you're saying, Carla, is very serious. I don't really know why you're saying it at all, and I'm not going to be such a hypocrite as to pretend you're welcome any longer in this house!'

'How naïve you are!' Carla made a little graceful gesture with her hand. 'In spite of your cleverness, your pleasant position in society, you're starved for your own husband's love. He gives you a big allowance and you play the grand lady, but inside you must weep!'

'Why should I?' Brooke heard herself saying calmly, though her distaste for Carla was written plainly in her face. 'My husband treats me with gentleness, consideration and understanding. Innocent little Lucia is happy, away from your malice, and you can't hurt me. I don't want to push you rudely through the door, but I'd like you to go. We simply do *not* compete!'

'Poor tragic little bride!' Carla persisted inexorably. 'I'm glad we had this interesting little talk.' Her dark hair curled about her face and her large eyes were glittering with feeling. 'No need to call for Gianni. I'll show myself out.' She laughed with what seemed like real delight and took herself swiftly out on to the portico, then downstairs into the sunlight.

Brooke stood there watching for some time, then she turned as Lucia addressed her.

'Has she gone?'

'I told her to.'

'I'm glad!' Lucia moved across the marble floor and slipped an arm around Brooke's waist. 'Now we can have coffee, just the two of us. Carla is a troublemaker. It has always been so. Zia Anna never really liked her, but at least she thought she would be company for me on the trip over. Papa paid for her, of course, but she was supposed to return.'

'Ah well, let's have our coffee.' Brooke turned the younger girl around, praying her face wouldn't betray her. There was precious little lightheartedness left in her now, but she had to cover up for Lucia's sake. 'Afterwards, why don't you ring Kate and Melissa? Gianni has cleaned the pool out and Harry would be pleased to help you get a barbecue luncheon.'

'Oh, could I?' Lucia's pansy-soft eyes showed her pleasure.

'You don't even have to ask!' Brooke said with affection. 'This is your home as well as mine. I like to see you happy with your friends!'

Harriet, coming through from the kitchen with a silver tray, asked: 'In the sun room?' She knew well enough that the tempestuous Miss di Campo had departed.

'Yes, thank you, Harry,' Brooke nodded absently. 'Sit down and have one with us.'

'I won't say no to it,' Harry returned pleasantly. 'Now what's this I hear about some young people coming out?'

'Only two, Harry,' said Lucia, whirling around.

'All I want is numbers so I can nourish them!' Harriet returned, smiling. 'No problem in this house!'

There was something about her young mistress's face that was worrying her, but she was too tactful to say anything.

Later on in the day when the girls were enjoying themselves by the pool, Gianni came through to announce that Mrs Symons had called in to say hello. Brooke got up immediately in a kind of confused gratitude. An hour or so before she had taken a call from Maggie and some of her mood must have communicated itself to her friend. Maggie's business kept her very fully occupied and Brooke knew she had taken time off specially to call in and see her.

Maggie was standing in the drawing room, handling with reverence a pottery court lady of the T'ang dynasty. She was passionately devoted to Chinese ceramics and owned a valuable collection herself, most of it inherited from an old uncle who had been a well-known art gallery curator.

'Maggie, how nice of you to call!'

'You worried me on the phone, dear!' Maggie put the pottery figure down and kissed Brooke's cheek in her usual warm, friendly manner. 'Just you tell your Aunt Maggie. Lillian isn't here, nor Louise, and you know quite well I'm extremely fond of you.'

'You're almost too good to me, Maggie,' Brooke said quietly. 'By the way, Lucia will want to thank you for her pendant. She loved it.'

'Nothing at all!' Generous Maggie brushed the pretty little Art Nouveau gift away. 'She thanked me very nicely on the phone. She's really a delightful little girl and you're extraordinarily good with her.'

'That's easy,' said Brooke. 'She's so grateful to belong, to put her roots down. She's made friends with some of my girls too. They're out at the pool now, having a lovely time. Harry put on a lovely lunch—not that I was able to eat any.'

'And why not?' Maggie took the armchair to the left of the sofa.

Brooke brooded on it, her golden-green eyes darkening to jade. 'I had rather an upsetting visit from Carla this morning. A very brief visit. I had to ask her to leave.'

Maggie's intelligent face looked disturbed. 'I don't like that young lady. She's very attractive, I grant you, but there's something ... *sly*, is that the word? ... there.'

'That's not the only word we can arrive at,' Brooke answered dryly, though her pent-up feelings were robbing her of her bright natural colour.

'Then tell me,' Maggie invited, still frowning. 'It has something to do with Paul, of course.'

'Yes, it has.' Brooke stared back at her. 'Can I offer you something, Maggie?'

'No, dear.' Maggie shook her head. 'Just tell me what's making your heart ache.'

'Does it show?'

'I know that much about you. Carla has been trying to make mischief, hasn't she?'

'Maybe she was simply telling the truth,' Brooke said strangely. She clasped her hands together in a convulsive little movement, then bent her bright head to stare at them. 'I couldn't tell anyone else but you, Maggie, but I feel utterly tormented and I can't help it. Things aren't right with my marriage and I think Carla knows it.'

'My dearest child!' Maggie said in a strong, comforting tone. 'I know your husband worships you.'

'No, Maggie!'

'Well, if he doesn't, he deserves an Academy Award.'

'All Italians are good actors,' shrugged Brooke.

'Are you trying to tell me Carla claims Paul is interested in *her*?' Maggie almost shouted.

'Yes,' Brooke whispered, and swallowed hard. 'You see, Maggie, ours is a compassionate marriage, not a passionate one. He wanted certain things from the beginning ...'

'He wanted you!' said Maggie, gasping and numb.

'He wants a house and a family.'

'Well?'

'Well, he doesn't sleep with me!' Brooke burst out, driven and full of grief.

Maggie pushed herself up out of the armchair and came to sit beside her on the sofa. 'But, my dear child, whose idea was this? Not Paul's, surely. One can scarcely start a family from separate rooms.'

'I want him to *love* me, Maggie!' Brooke said intensely. 'He's never mentioned love once.'

'Have you?'

'Of course not!' Brooke said, stammering a little. 'I'd feel such a fool. You see how attractive he is to women—they practically fling themselves at him. Why should *I*?'

'I'd advise you to do it if you want to hold on to your husband!' Maggie answered dryly.

'You make it sound the simplest thing in the world,' Brooke murmured with increasing unhappiness.

'It should be if you love him,' Maggie pointed out gently. 'Do you, my dear?'

'I hardly know!' Brooke gave a little shudder. 'I miss him every minute I don't see him. I love the look of him and the sound of him, the way he sings in the morning just to amuse me. He knows every opera that was ever written, every pop tune. He's an amazing man. He rushes around every part of the country and he works fantastic hours, yet he never get tired. He loves Lucia and she adores him, but mostly he regards me as a young sister.'

'Good gracious!' said Maggie, her voice marvelling. 'The whole situation is absolutely mad! Say what you will, dear, I've seen Paul looking at you, and so help me if a man ever looked at me like that, I'd live on it for the rest of my days.'

'What if it's true, what Carla says?'

'You still haven't told me what she did say.'

Brooke's mouth quivered and she bit her lip. 'I don't think it was worth repeating, but it gave me a shock. I can't stop thinking about it.'

Maggie's expression grew thoughtful and she patted Brooke's hand. 'You sound to me as if you're very much in love with your husband. That being the case, you'll have to work at making a success of your marriage. Most of us think it *is* a success. Both of you present a very beautiful front—the best I've seen at any rate. You always had great potential, but you've positively bloomed since your marriage. You can't tell me Paul hasn't tried to make love to you.'

Brooke looked up at her friend with a curious expression. 'Am I mad to care whether he loves me or not?'

'I think he does!' Maggie challenged her. 'Listen, dear, no woman can afford to lock her husband out of her bedroom—not if she cares about him and wants to hold on to her marriage. The only advice I can give you is to ignore Carla and practise setting your husband's heart pounding. There's a fire in you, why not let him see it?'

Brooke pushed her titian mane over her shoulder. 'I might get more than I bargain for. Paul is no ordinary man.'

'Isn't that the truth?' said Maggie, trying for lightness. 'Carla has hurt you, but I'd simply refuse to believe her.'

'She had Paul's lighter. The one I gave him soon after we arrived home. It doesn't pay to leave things about.'

'I fancy she's just jealous!' Maggie said sharply. 'And she could have picked it up anywhere. She was here at the party last week.'

'Then Paul has taken a long time to miss it.' said Brooke, her face intent and serious. 'I can't change my nature, Maggie. I know marriage is a very serious business, that many things are expected of me, but I refuse point blank to share my husband. That would be too cruel, too degrading.'

'It's also out of character for Paul,' Maggie insisted with unwonted irritability. 'He has too much finesse, too much integrity to be taken in by a little bit of spice like Carla. You can't keep questioning him over and over because he's a very attractive man. It's too bad you haven't got more confidence in yourself. You're looking wonderful these days. It shouldn't take the slightest effort to reach your husband. I'm sure, now, you haven't even tried.'

'No, I haven't because I thought ... oh, it doesn't matter.'

Maggie watched her, the shining bent head, the soft drooping mouth. 'Take my advice, dear, and get out your flimsiest nightgown tonight!'

By the time Brooke was ready for bed, she was whiter than ever. All through dinner she had been very quiet and Lucia had looked at her anxiously. Paul had rung to say he wouldn't be home until much later in the evening. There were problems with the new high-rise building down near the waterfront and the architects were coming in. Brooke had taken the call in a strange apathy, but not for a minute did she consider checking. It wasn't what she expected out of her marriage and she wasn't prepared to do it. It went completely against the grain. Nevertheless, she suffered the dreadful uncertainty Carla had bequeathed to her.

Shortly after Lucia had gone off to bed, the phone rang. Gianni answered it, but when Brooke came out into the hallway he told her with a graphic shrug that no one had answered and he hung up again. Ten minutes later it rang again and this time Brooke took the call. After the third hello she stopped. There was someone at the other end, but they obviously weren't going to talk. Disturbed, Brooke went to hang up, and it was then she heard the soft, muffled giggle. 'Who's there?' she said sharply, but the line went dead.

'What is it, *signora?*' Gianni stood watching her, a tall distinguished blur, because her heart was thumping so hard.

'A nuisance call, I think!'

'*So!*' Gianni drew in his breath and his face went rigid. 'Allow me to attend to this, *signora.*'

'Thank you, Gianni.' Her head was slightly bent, but she smiled at him.

'*A servirla, signora.* Do you wish for anything else?'

'No, I think I'll follow Lucia's example and have a reasonably early night. *Buona notte*, Gianni. You make things very easy for me.'

'Then I am happy!' Gianni bowed with great style and Brooke, watching him, approved of him more than ever. 'Paolo will be here shortly,' he added as if Brooke was in dire need of her husband's presence.

'I don't think so.' His smile could not reassure her, or his words. Unless her imagination was playing tricks on her that detestable gurgle was Carla's. She had heard her many times laugh deeply in her throat like that. Was that what the phone call was all about? To explain it all to her; the whole unhealthy situation. Gianni was reading her distress, for he was looking at her searchingly but gently.

In her room she decided to wash herself clean of her wretchedness. She walked to the adjoining bathroom and ran the bath, pouring in a preparation that turned the tub into a scented sea of foamy bubbles, coloured a blush rose. Later, lying back in the scented water with her hair pinned to the top of her head, she tried to relax. She had been brought up to believe good manners were all-important, but she would like another chance at telling Carla just what she thought of her.

'Darling?'

She heard Paul's voice and sat up quickly, then slid down again.

'Brooke, where are you?'

He sounded madly impatient to see her, volatile, demanding, and she wondered afresh at the many faces he presented. He must have come through the connecting door, because she could hear the soft thud of his footsteps in her bedroom.

'I'm in the bath!' she called out in frantic modesty. The rosy bubbles made a gauzy veil for her slender body and she was incredibly shy of him. She slid down lower to protect herself, stricken by the fact he was most certainly going to walk into the bathroom.

He was unashamedly uninhibited, though she had to admit he had always shown scrupulous regard for her privacy.

'Well, well, well!' he said softly. He came to the doorway, resting against the jamb, his black eyes full of admiration and sparkling laughter. 'Who said pink did not suit redheads?' He was wearing a beautiful lightweight summer suit and he looked very handsome and vital.

Brooke could have strangled him, but her eyes dropped and her colour heightened. 'I'll be out in a minute!'

'Of course you will, silly! I have a drink ready for both of us. It has been such a terrible day, but you're something special to come home to.'

His voice was deliberately caressing her, lovemaking from a distance, and she could feel the curious answering tingling sensation right through her body. 'Go away!' she begged him.

There was excitement and brilliance in his liquid black eyes. 'I realise you're very shy, very modest, but I am your husband, Surely I don't matter?'

'You *do*!' She was agonisingly aware of him and the disappearing bubbles.

He stood looking down at her with a faintly mocking, faintly quizzical expression, then he laughed and turned away. 'Don't be long. You know I hate to drink alone.'

The moment he disappeared Brooke started up and grabbed for a pink towel, huge and velvety, somehow perfumed with sunshine and roses. She stepped out of the bath on to the thick rug, drying herself hastily, avoiding her own delightful reflection. She looked around the room, then made a small sound of distress as she realised she had no clothes to put on, not even a robe.

'Hey, what's keeping you?' Paul was back, looking so flamboyantly male he made her think of some dark, dashing buccaneer invading her boudoir and her bath. He had taken off his jacket and tie and loosened the tiny pearly buttons of his finely striped shirt so she could see the dark mat of hair on his chest and the gold glint of the medallion he always wore. He was arrogant, super-positive and super-masculine, and perhaps this very night he had betrayed her.

All over again she could hear Carla's hateful, breathy giggle and her golden-green eyes went huge and accusing. 'You're home earlier than I expected.'

'Must you sound like that?' There was a little break in his vibrant voice and in the next instant he was behind her, drawing her back against him, lowering his dark head to drink in her fragrance, pressing little kisses all along the sensitive cord of her neck. 'Don't speak like that to me, little one. It has been a long day and I've longed for the sight of you!'

Brooke could see their multiple mirrored reflections and it gave her a little shock, so for a moment she leaned back against his hard body. She had never realised before how dark he was or how fair she seemed in comparison. Their images were erotic, disturbing her, and she looked away.

'*Brooke!*' he murmured. There was a delirious sensuality in his voice and a dominance.

'No!' she whispered. 'No more.'

'Be still now!' He lifted her easily and though she cried out he carried her back into her quiet bedroom, lowering her on to the big fourposter bed with its silken bedspread and hangings. Her hair had come loose from its confining pins and it tumbled all around her flushed face and bare shoulders. She lay staring up at him with a breathless panic in her face much like some small wild creature confonting its hunter.

'What is this expression? What are you afraid of?' One finger lay hard along her cheek, but he made no further move to touch her.

Brooke made a desperate effort to cover her fright. 'Maybe I'm frigid!' she said hazily. She sat up and pulled the towel more closely around her, though she knew he had seen the tips of her breasts.

'That's nice!' His tenderness and gaiety seemed to be turning to anger and a hard, mocking control. 'You look so lovely and inviting!'

Horrified, she could see now that he had brought home masses and masses of roses of the most beautiful deep crimson, cramming them into the big Oriental blossom jar from the hallway. 'They're beautiful!' Two crystal tumblers stood beside the roses, their sides frosted, ice jingling, and she took a long, inadequate breath.

'Ah, you've noticed!' he reproached her. 'You feel ashamed!'

'I'm no good for you, Paul,' she said doggedly. 'You know how I feel. I'm hopeless at pretending.'

'I know what you tell me!' he countered, moving to sit down on the bed beside her. 'Is anything wrong? Something I should know about?'

The light gleamed on her titian hair and her flawless skin, got caught in her eyes. In that moment her beauty was ravishing, woven of many things, her déshabille, her acute femininity and innocence, her sweetly sensuous capacity to arouse this stranger, her husband, in a way she did not intend. 'Of course nothing's wrong,' she said with great difficulty.

'So?' His black eyes seemed to be consuming her, moving from her head to the tips of her toes. 'Gianni told me you seemed pale and upset. Now you are blushing like a rose, though I've scarcely touched you. That is your flower, I think, the rose. So memorable, so sweetly scented and romantic.'

'I'm sorry!' her fingers fluttered as though excusing herself and she moved a little away from him. 'I'm not right for you, Paul!'

'Not yet,' he agreed crisply, 'but right or wrong, you are mine and I do not intend to ever let you go.' He spoke quietly, but it sounded so implacable she bent her body away from him.

'But our bargain! I can't give you anything ... never!'

'So hysterical!' his tone mocked her. 'No more drama, *cara*, please no more. What you can't give, I'll take. I know you don't love me, but you will love our child.' His eyes moved from her face to the shadowed cleft of her breast and the long narrow waist.

Brooke didn't answer, staring at him, and only when he reached for her did she find her voice. 'Surely you haven't forgotten your promise?'

'I've gone through hell remembering!' he told her with harsh humour. 'You make me very angry—all this fire and ice. You are perfect, I want only to love you, yet you talk such terrible nonsense. Everything is different now. You can't give me anything. Such a foolish child, when I so badly want a woman!'

A wild fit of jealousy seized her. 'That's a joke, is it?' she cried bitterly. 'I mean, how many women in a day are necessary?'

His hands that held her tightly at the waist dropped away. 'Are you mad?'

'Not in the least!' She opened wide her luminous green eyes. 'You think you're wonderful, so clever, Paul Corelli. Maybe I've found you out!'

For several seconds he stared at her, his winged black brows drawing together. 'You *are* mad!' he snapped, flinging her away from him so she fell like a tossed flower against the heaped nest of pillows. There was a flickering dangerous light in the depths of his eyes, a hard tension in his lithe graceful body. 'I do not have unlimited patience, perhaps you will tell me what you're talking about.' Abruptly he moved away from her and walked to the little Louis Quinze escritoire picking up his drink and tossing it off with bitter satisfaction. 'Well, what are these rumours, these whispers that have so shocked your virgin ears?'

Brooke felt utterly naked, her whole body flushing and on fire. 'I want to put on my nightgown!' she said stormily.

'What for?' he flashed back, with a twist of his mouth.

'Stop it, Paul!'

'This my home, isn't it? If I wish to look at my wife, I will. Surely you don't expect me to leave, or do you? I assure you I won't. Come, *signorina*,' he stressed cruelly, 'am I never to hear what you mean by your outrageous statement?'

'*Please!*' she said again, and her full mouth quivered. 'I always said you'd know how to make a woman suffer.'

'Really?' He smiled ironically, and came back towards her with his smooth, rhythmic stride. 'I thought I was being exceptionally good to you.'

'Then do what I ask!' she cried out in agitation,

feeling helpless and trapped and scarcely clothed. 'Go away and leave me alone.'

'*Never!*'

A strange little tremor shot through her, an awareness that she was pushing him too far. His control with her had been monumental, even as his passion might be volcanic.

'I've tried every way I know how to fulfil your demands,' he told her, 'now it's time for you to fulfil mine!'

'And if I can't?' her heart was pounding and her ears were filled with a roar like the surf dashing itself up against a rock wall.

'Then at least we will be very much married!' He was standing over her, very dark and sleek, his eyes never leaving her face. Slowly he began to unbutton his shirt and a sense of utter fatality enveloped her.

'I'm going to fight you,' she whispered.

'Fight me, darling. It doesn't matter!' He reached for her and pulled her into his arms, his beautiful hard body beside her, taking her face firmly between his hands and covering her mouth with his own.

He was still holding her when she could resist him no longer and she could feel the melting weakness spread through her body, sensation piling on sensation, bewildering her because there seemed no release. Hazily she realised he was speaking to her in his own language, his hands covering her body, bringing her to a feverish ardency, until she no longer had the desire to evade him. Such caresses were leaving her mindless, her body accepting him as the perfect lover. Though she didn't even realise it, her arms were up and around his neck, clinging, her mouth young and ardent, moving under his own, her trembling body silken and yielding.

'You belong to me. You always have done, since you were born. *Say* it!' He twisted his hand through her hair so she had to open her eyes.

'No.' She was too vulnerable, too fevered and shocked by her own feelings.

'No matter, your body is saying it for you. Tell me to leave you and I will.'

'You're cruel ... a tormentor!' Even as the words left her throat, Paul's mouth stopped her.

'For *you* to say that!' he said huskily. 'You who have tormented me day and night!' He wrapped his hand in her hair kissing her deeply. 'Say you want me.'

'Yes.' Her shaken whisper was very low, but he heard her.

He shifted her in his arms, his dark face elated, strong yet gentle, masterful and tender, a combination of qualities that left her weak with desire. Lingeringly his hands travelled over her, moving to cup her tender, yearning breasts, taking the soft weight of them.

'How beautiful you are!' he said with infinite tenderness, and bent his head.

Brooke stiffened and gave a little stifled moan, then she gave herself up to her tumultuous feelings, not stopping him because she loved him and she wanted him and the pleasure of having him beside her in this way was shattering. Her eyes were half shut and her lips parted. He was speaking to her in words she didn't understand, but the meaning was obvious. Passion rose between them and he was wonderfully confident. Instinctively she followed wherever he led her, for nothing else in the whole world seemed to matter.

CHAPTER EIGHT

BROOKE woke late next morning to find herself alone. Without Paul beside her, she experienced an incredible sense of separation and she wondered why, after such a night, she had failed to tell him how much she loved him. His physical reality lingered beside her and she reached over and stroked the cool, smooth sheet and the pillow on which he had laid his dark head. He had awoken her to such a pitch she ached for him. He had been the most perfect lover and her clear, creamy skin flushed with colour. For the first time in her life she was fully conscious and proud of being a woman. Paul had made her completely whole, and though she felt the same melting sensations he aroused in her, there was warmth and peace too, like a homecoming.

She would ring him. Speak to him. Tell him she loved him. She was devastated by the sweeping rush of emotion she felt for him. There had been a kind of glory about the night, the fascination of sweet violence and afterwards a superb tenderness. She stretched slowly and languorously, arching her neck and her spine. She wanted him again. She would never stop wanting him until her heart ceased to beat. Or had he said that? He had taken her with such passion, such piercing beauty and excitement, it didn't seem possible she was not the only, beloved woman in his life. The incredible feeling of closeness remained with her and she was certain Paul felt it too. They were no longer separate people, but part of each other, and it seemed a vital necessity for her to get up and ring him.

Her green eyes blazed with excitement and she thrust her long slender legs out of bed. She was naked for the first time in her life, but even that didn't seem to matter. Paul had told her over and over again in such moving, exciting ways that her woman's body gave him utter, complete delight, an incredible feeling of power. In a second she had her robe on, walking to the window, looking out over the beautiful garden. How sweet was the morning, how scented the air, how gay and restored she felt in mind and body. Carla and her breathless little accusations didn't even come into her mind. The very air seemed sprinkled with gold dust and the erotic excitement of the night persisted, giving her a startling beauty. Quickly she wound her hair up on the top of her head, fixed it with a few pins and went through to the bathroom to turn on the shower. The day offered such promise and tonight Paul would be home. Confidence and elation stirred in her. Paul, her husband.

As it turned out, Brooke was unable to get her call through. Paul's secretary told her regretfully that Mr Corelli had been called away and she was uncertain of the time he would return to his office; there were structural problems associated with a new downtown site and Mr Corelli was expected to call there first. If the matter was urgent Mr Corelli could certainly be contacted, but Brooke said pleasantly that no, the matter wasn't urgent and she would see her husband that evening. She only wanted to tell her husband she loved him. Nothing more urgent than that, but it made her catch her breath and her face break out into smiles as she encountered and said good morning to every member of the household. There were even yellow roses, glistening with dew, that the gardener had brought in to Harriet first thing in the morning and she had promptly placed in the centre of the breakfast table like some beautiful, glowing omen.

On that day everything seemed admirable. There was overseas mail from Mamma and Louise giving a good ten-page account of their shopping and sight-seeing and the wonderful house parties they had been to. It all sounded very impressive to Brooke, but not surprising. Mamma was a born hedonist and she was well suited to a way of life others might have found superficial or exhausting.

Brooke was sitting out on the sundeck watching Lucia perfecting her dive from the side of the pool when the call came. There was nothing to warn her. The sun was in her eyes, so she didn't really see Gianni's expression, but when he spoke she sat up straight and swung her legs to the redwood decking.

'Paul!' she said faintly, and gave a little betraying lurch.

'Please, *signora*!' Automatically Gianni put his hand to her elbow to steady her. 'They said only he had been taken to hospital for observation, to check on the extent of his injuries. There was an accident ... some member of the construction crew ... Paolo went to his aid, but he was injured himself. I confess I am so upset I never heard all that Mr Collins was telling me. He is the construction boss or some such thing. At first I thought ...'

'Don't, Gianni!' Brooke took off her sunglasses and behind them her eyes looked larger, the colour deeper, and yet their expression was frightened and somehow unfocused. Gianni, beside her, was bent over like the old man he really was and she shook her head trying to clear it. 'I must go to the hospital. Lucia must be told. I'm so afraid, Gianni. Why didn't you call me to the phone?'

'Signor Collins rang off. He insisted I break the news to you gently. He sounded very shocked himself and there were many things he had to do himself.'

'All right, Gianni,' Brooke murmured bleakly, 'I understand.' She shuddered as the full realisation began to hit her in waves. 'I woke up so happy. I tried to ring him, you know. Please tell Bob to get the car out for me and leave it standing in the drive, then go back inside and lie down. You've had a shock. I know how devoted you are to my husband. I'll ring you from the hospital. We might find that his injuries aren't serious. I pray to God that is so—I don't think I could survive without him.'

'And little Lucia?' Gianni looked towards the brilliant aquamarine pool where Lucia was exercising her slight limbs.

'I'll tell her now. She can come with me. She'll want to see her father.' Brooke twisted her titian head around and called to the girl, who looked up smiling and waved.

'Why don't you come in yourself? It's heavenly!'

'Oh, God!' whispered Brooke, and began to tremble.

Gianni's hand touched her shoulder, then he walked towards the edge of the pool calling to Lucia in their own language. He was standing there to help her out of the water, her black hair wet and her brown skin glistening, then Brooke saw him put his arm around her shoulder as she began to cry.

'Lucia dear,' she spoke gently, 'we must get ready to go to the hospital. You want to come with me, don't you?'

'Si, certainly!' Lucia looked up and her little face firmed with purpose, but Brooke could see the fear and bewilderment in her eyes.

The pallor of Brooke's own face was pronounced. Somehow she got them all moving, her hands tightly clenched and her jaw tight to stop herself from crying. Harriet had been told, and Brooke was grateful to her for the way she attended to both Gianni and Lucia in their shaken states. Brooke herself maintained a strange ominous silence. She tried to pray, but nothing seemed to come. Paul wasn't dead, though the terror touched her. She dressed quickly, not really conscious of anything she put on. Her skin felt cold, yet it was a warm, golden day. Surely God in His mercy couldn't take Paul away from her? She loved him, yet she hadn't even told him. If anything happened to him she would never forgive herself for all the days of her life. Nothing mattered but Paul and what he had come to mean to her. He had wanted her to have his child. He had wanted so much more of her, and she had withheld herself while he covered her and her whole family with gifts. She had even accused him falsely of an involvement with Carla when she knew in her heart of hearts that Carla had reached him in no way at all. Perhaps she was was going to be punished now. Perhaps she was going to be left alone with Wintersweet and Paul's only child, Lucia. Lucia she loved, but she loved Paul much, much more. More than she had ever loved anything or anyone in her whole life. Without him she would be desolate for ever.

A tear fell and she put a hand to her cheek, wiping it ruthlessly away. She had to be the strong one, at least until they reached the hospital. Lucia was little more than a child and her father meant everything in the world to her. Lucia, too, would be feeling this terrible, lancing pain. She wished she had spoken to the Mr Collins who had rung the house. Probably he had no real idea of the extent of Paul's injuries. They could be internal.

'Paul!' she whispered, and ran downstairs.

The traffic was heavy all the way to the hospital and she could have screamed with anguished frustration. Lucia sat beside her, huddled up in deep thought. There was nothing to say, nothing they could do until they found out how Paul was. Tension was building up in Brooke at such a rate she had to make a great effort to even release her breath. She thought of Paul, so wonderfully fit and hard, the way his body had so perfectly fitted her own, and her face twisted in protest. She couldn't bear to think of that same beautiful male body bruised and crushed. Gianni had told her some section of a wall had collapsed.

Somehow they found parking close to the main entrance and Brooke raced away to the desk to make her enquiries. The woman there was kind but collected. For twenty years she had dealt with the public, but never once had she known the personal, heart-pounding fright of involvement. She spoke to a nurse and the nurse in turn looked at Brooke and issued a command.

'Come this way!'

'Lucia!' Brooke looked back and held out her hand and Lucia quickly closed the gap between them, clinging to Brooke's hand and following the nurse's determined lead. There seemed to be patients everywhere, sitting, standing, dressing or undressing in cubicles. This was Casualty and apparently Paul had not yet been admitted to a ward. Brooke forced her mind to focus on this. Surely it was a good sign. The nurse continued to walk calmly and with a necessary detachment through the ranks of injuries, but the pallor of Lucia's young face was alarming. Brooke pressed her hand, willing her a little control, though the familiar, unfamiliar, smell of the hospital was making her feel nauseated as well.

'Wait here, please.'

The nurse turned and gave them a smile that helped, indicating a vacant bench with her hand.

Brooke and Lucia sat close together, staring down at the drab floor, both of them grateful they weren't alone, but both of them unbearably tense. A few minutes elapsed, then a tall, grey-haired man with intent blue eyes emerged from the end surgery and came towards them.

'Mrs Corelli?'

Brooke jumped to her feet, her heart thumping. She faced the doctor with her whole heart in her eyes, seeing the tiredness and strain in his face. 'How is my husband, doctor?'

The doctor sighed and took off his glasses. 'I think, young lady, you can offer up a big prayer of thankfulness. He's all right, but I'd like to keep him here for a day or two. It would be wise to keep an eye on him with a head injury. No broken bones like the other poor chap who, I understand, was responsible for the accident. Your husband went to his assistance, and incidentally saved his life.'

'Can I see him?' In her sick haste Brooke forgot to include Lucia, then she remembered and explained that Lucia was Paul's daughter.

The doctor nodded politely and considered. 'For a moment only, then I want him admitted. He recovered consciousness only once and then briefly. Mercifully

signs of damage to the brain are absent and it's simply
a matter of waiting until he comes around. The workman's injuries aren't serious considering. He's deeply
shocked and holds himself responsible and he's taken a
certain amount of calming down. I don't think he'll
be properly convinced until your husband is up and
about, Mrs Corelli. But come this way, both of you.
Just a moment, but I know you'll feel happier to see
him. Only one scalp laceration, but he has plenty of
thick black hair!'

Brooke's heart was fluttering violently, and Lucia's
face already beginning to pucker. Paul was lying on
the table, his face unmarked, the sculptured mouth
and the eyelids closed, a bandage binding his wide fore-
head and his dark hair. His head was turned a little
to the left and his arms lay slackly by his side. There
was no colour whatever in his face or his mouth and the
bone structure seemed very clean beneath the taut
skin.

'Oh, Paul!' Brooke felt the jolt to her heart. She
stood at the side of the table looking down at him
and Lucia moved to the other side and looked down at
the quiet face of her father.

'The wound to the head is superficial,' the doctor
said quietly. 'The X-ray report is good. Still, he'll have
to be watched. Reflexes are normal. He's a very lucky
man and he's very fit and strong. I should go home
now and phone in from time to time. There's no
reason for you to worry.'

'We can't help it!' Brooke answered for both of
them. 'Thank you, doctor, I know he's in good hands.'

All through the rest of the day and the night Brooke
tried to feel the comfort of her own words. Paul *was*

in good hands. His doctor, she had learned later, was a distinguished neuro-surgeon and senior consultant to the hospital. She didn't sleep much, so anxious it was a real physical pain, and she kept listening for the phone to ring. Once she woke up in a sweat thinking she had heard its shrill call, then she fell back to the pillows again, saying to herself in a long, gasping breath:

'It's all right. Everything is going to be all right!'

In the morning she had a headache and the whole household was upset and withdrawn. Conquering her distress and anxiety, Brooke rang the hospital and received the news that her husband's condition was satisfactory and he had recovered consciousness during the night. She had asked with difficulty what time she could see him and was told the normal visiting hours.

'How is he?'

They were all grouped around her; Lucia and Gianni and Harriet, their eyes raying through her. 'Condition satisfactory!' Brooke repeated the message, then burst into tears.

'There now!' Harriet patted her shoulder. 'I'll go make us all a cup of tea. Everything will be all right now. You'll see!'

A spasm crossed Brooke's eyes and she put out a hand to Lucia, who took Brooke's hand firmly in her own.

'I'll stay here when you go up and see Papa. He will want to see you.'

'Sh-sh! We'll both go and if he is very much better then Gianni will want to see him as well.'

'Thank you, *signora*!' Gianni bowed and his face lost its aged, forlorn look. 'I have prayed and the good God has heard me!'

The time passed slowly, but then they were at the hospital and Lucia insisted gently that Brooke go in to see Paul first. He had a private room and though his eyes were shut, he knew the instant she walked in the door.

'Brooke!'

He pulled himself up in the bed and she went to him swiftly. 'No, please, Paul. Lie quietly.'

'But why?' He sounded faintly surprised.

'You're in a hospital and you've had quite a blow to your head.' She looked at him appealingly, her golden-green eyes shadowed from lack of sleep. 'How are you? Don't move, if it will hurt you. Lucia is waiting just outside the door. You gave us all such a terrible fright!'

'Please, little one!' he checked her nervous flow of words, 'Lucia, in a moment, first tell me why you look this way?' His black eyes were looking into hers in the same brilliant way.

'You *know*. I was so very worried and afraid.'

He framed her face between his hands. 'Then kiss me.'

'It might be bad for you, so soon!'

'Little fool!' He held her head firmly, a kind of reproach in his dark eyes, then he covered her mouth with his own.

'I love you!' Her fingers clenched around his own.

'Do you?' He was looking at her searchingly.

'Terribly!' Her eyes fell and she kissed his hand. 'I hope you'll let me tell you how much when you get home.'

'Of course I will!' There seemed to be a dangerous light in his eyes and he hadn't lost his mocking smile. 'I'm sorry I had to frighten you, my beautiful wife. You look as if you've been through a time of confusion and fear, a small crisis.'

'The biggest of my life!' she said in a voice that shook slightly. 'I must let Lucia in. It's been a distressing time for her as well.'

'M-m, do that, my darling,' said Paul, looking at her for a moment with searching attention. 'I should very much like to see her. If everything turns out all right, I should be home tomorrow.'

'Oh, I hope so!' Brooke said fervently, and turning away, missed the expression on her husband's face.

Lucia came in in a little fearful rush, then as she saw her father looking so absolutely normal, an overwhelming thankfulness turned her knees to water.

'Oh, Papa!' she exclaimed, and hunched against his breast.

Miraculously Paul was discharged the next day and his doctor overrode all Brooke's remaining fears and anxieties. Paul's memory of the incident was complete right until the crucial second before he hurled himself and his workman clear of the main danger zone when the slightest miscalculation could have killed them both, and all his tests were clear. There was no further cause for anxiety and Paul had taken the time to visit Tom Doyle, his workman, on the third floor, reassuring him by his presence even though Tom realised he had a few things to answer for when he got out of hospital. At least the boss was all right, and that blotted out his main fear.

The phone had been ringing for most of the day, mostly to support Brooke, then when she informed all her callers that Paul was coming home that day, they greeted the news with sincere pleasure and relief. Carla rang as well, Gianni and Brooke converging on the phone simultaneously, but Brooke mouthed to Gianni with confidence that she would take the call after he ascertained who was ringing and took the receiver out of his hand.

'Brooke here, Carla!' she said clearly.

'When is Paul coming home?' Carla cut her short.

'Today.'

'You mean it?'

'I mean there's nothing more I'm going to tell you,' Brooke said calmly. 'You played your hand and lost. My husband is coming home this afternoon and you can speak to him some other time if you wish. As a gentleman and a distant relative he's bound to answer you, but nothing more, Carla—not that I would enjoy telling him your deliberate lies. Now, if you'll excuse me, I've many things to do. This is a day of celebration in our house!'

'But, Brooke——' Carla tried to hold her.

''Bye now!' said Brooke, and hung up with considerable satisfaction.

Dinner went off with a flourish, with Gianni serving looking twenty years younger and Lucia talking gaily without a trace of the little nervous stammer that sometimes assailed her. Brooke, though she was looking very slender and beautiful, was rather quiet as though her days and nights of anxiety had almost consumed her nervous energy. Paul had been spared to her and that was all she could seem to remember. He sat at the head of the table with the light from the chandelier playing all over the planes and angles of his dark face and she couldn't seem to get enough of the sight of it. Did he really know how she cared?

Later when she prepared for bed she did the only thing she could think of doing. She touched perfume to her wrists and ears and the valley between her breasts and changed into a gown and robe from her beautiful trousseau, a delicate shade of peach that harmonised perfectly with her colouring. Love and desire were like a fever within her, though she was deeply aware Paul had been giving her brilliant, disarming glances all evening. Perhaps he didn't believe in her frantic declaration of love. Perhaps he was convinced it was only the result of shock. The pattern of their life, shaped over the past months, would have completely changed if anything had happened to him. Paul was the all-powerful figure in their lives. They were all dependent on him, even Mamma and Louise, so busy enjoying themselves overseas.

She walked towards his room and hesitated at the door. 'Paul?'

He turned and looked at her, a little curiously, she thought. 'Yes, darling?'

'Would you like anything?' Her heart was melting at the sight of him.

'I want you here,' he said smoothly, 'so you can finish confiding in me.'

'You know all my secrets now!'

'I know you told me you loved me in the urgency of a moment. What I don't know is whether you really meant it or if you felt desperately insecure.'

She couldn't answer him, but gave an involuntary little shiver. Something was aching at the base of her throat and she put a hand to it instinctively. The light was moving along her hair, the curve of her cheek, caressing her body beneath the nearly sheer gown she wore. 'How odd it is that you don't believe me.'

'Come here!' he said a little roughly. 'Maybe I daren't believe you.'

Brooke's heart turned over, but she moved towards him and he pulled her down on to the bed, lying beside her and turning her slowly towards him. 'Are you sorry you married me?'

'No,' she said with sudden spirit, though she had gone rather white. 'I told you——'

'Be quiet, darling. I've waited a long time, so you may have to go on saying you love me for a long time as well.'

'Would the rest of our lives be fair?'

Paul drew a sharp little breath and put out his hand, sliding the thin strap of her nightgown off her shoulder, letting his hand linger before it slid downwards over her breast. 'You love me, yet you feel I'm not to be trusted?'

His desire was being communicated to her, yet there was a faint bitterness in his tone. 'I had no right,' she said uncertainly.

'No, you didn't!' he agreed, and pushed her night-gown right off her shoulders. 'Do you really think I could be with you and want someone else?'

'You've never told me you loved me!' She had to shut her eyes against the shattering arousal.

'It's you, my darling, who does not understand Italian. Some things in life we cannot control. I've wanted you since the first moment I laid eyes on you, and it has taken me all this time to make you mine!'

'Kiss me!' she begged with a little moan. He was caressing her with such skill, it seemed as if he was tormenting her.

'You won't fight me?'

'I told you I love you!'

'And I must be perfectly sure. You see, darling, I want your heart and your brain as well as this beautiful body you now offer me!' He bent his head and kissed her, just a brief pressure of his mouth, but a vast passion was behind it. 'Open your eyes!' he said gently. 'I want to look into your soul!' His arms went around her and he half held her up to him.

'What more can I tell you?' Her eyes met his and her hair tumbled back over his shoulder.

'Come, you can think of something!' His mouth touched her breast and he pressed her back against his arm. 'Could you live without me?'

'No!' She was taking in quick little breaths, her whole body flushed and ardent. 'The morning of your accident I tried to ring you. I wanted to tell you I loved you, how much you had taught me, but you were out, I couldn't get you, then that dreadful phone call in the afternoon! I thought I would lose you when I'd just discovered you were my life!'

For a split second every muscle in his body went taut. She looked up at him and heard his quickly indrawn breath. 'Don't say things like that if you don't mean it.'

'But it's true!' She lifted her hand with a sure instinct and placed a finger against the dent in his chin. 'I can't hide anything from you any more—I don't want to. I only want to reach you in any way I can. Like this, in your arms, when we're all alone and when we have people around us and, one day, our children. All I have to offer is yours!'

Paul's brilliant black eyes seemed to be blazing, all the uncertainty gone, and the smooth controlled manner. 'You know how vulnerable you make me?' he demanded. 'I have never belonged to any woman or wished to, but you are quite different. You have been from the beginning when you disturbed all my tranquillity. I think now I have been searching for you all my life. The sort of woman I never found who haunted me. And even when I did, you rejected me.'

'I can't imagine how!' Brooke said a little helplessly. 'I always knew you for the passionate man you are, but I wanted your love. It went very deep with me. Many women throw themselves at you without reticence or pride. I've seen them and I didn't want to be one of them. You don't know, but I couldn't have borne it if you had treated me with contempt!'

'Little fool!' he said in a low, vibrant tone, and dropped a kiss on her soft, parted mouth. 'I have always been extremely concerned with the way I treat you. You are very precious to me. Surely you know that by now?'

'I didn't know!' she pointed out gently. 'I was even jealous of Carla.'

'Carla!'

He sounded so profoundly shocked and yet arrogant, she had to smile. 'Yes, Carla. She hinted at many things, and she had the gold lighter I gave you.'

'So?' He looked down at her gleaming satiny skin and began to stroke it. 'I'm afraid I didn't tell you about the lighter. I put it down somewhere and I couldn't remember where. I've kept hoping I would find it again, and to the best of my knowledge I have never used it anywhere else but this house.'

'It's all right, darling, I believe you.'

'So you should!' he returned with slight disdain. 'Carla is a troublemaker, what you call a malicious person. Not always, but sometimes!'

'She's a big liar!' said Brooke.

'All right, she's a liar. What does it matter to us? We won't be seeing very much of her. I have a strong feeling she will soon be returning to Kenya. You should have told me she was disturbing you. I would have dealt with it.'

'Paolo!' She spoke his name in a voice full of tenderness.

'Nice!' He mocked her, but she could see the expression in his eyes. A wild sweetness surged through her, an inevitability.

'Love me!' she demanded, in an imperious little whisper.

'All the days of my life!'

His black eyes were smouldering, his dark face very close to her own. He lifted her arms and placed them around his neck, then he pulled her very close to him, fitting her slender feminine body to his own.

'My love. My own!'

Very tenderly, with rising passion, he placed his mouth over hers and began to kiss her slowly and deeply, as languorously as if they had all the time in the world, while Brooke responded with all the beauty and passion that was in her. Each answering the vow they had fervently promised for ever.

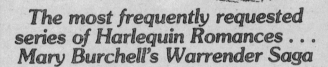

The Warrender Saga

The most frequently requested series of Harlequin Romances . . . Mary Burchell's Warrender Saga

Each complete novel is set in the exciting world of music and opera, spanning the years from the meeting of Oscar and Anthea in *A Song Begins* to his knighthood in *Remembered Serenade*. These nine captivating love stories introduce you to a cast of characters as vivid, interesting and delightful as the glittering, exotic locations. From the tranquil English countryside to the capitals of Europe— London, Paris, Amsterdam—the Warrender Saga will sweep you along in an unforgettable journey of drama, excitement and romance.

The Warrender Saga

The most frequently requested Harlequin Romance series

Free Special Bonus Offer

Purchase all 9 Warrender Saga novels and receive Mary Burchell's We Followed Our Stars as a Free Bonus.

We Followed Our Stars is the story of two sisters who crossed the Atlantic in the golden days of the 1920s, plunging into the glittering world of the opera . . . and later into the horrible brutality of Hitler's war-torn Europe. It's the real story of Ida Cook, a stenographer who became one of the world's most loved writers of romantic fiction—Mary Burchell.

$1.50 *if purchased separately!*

Complete and mail
this coupon today!

Harlequin Reader Service

In U.S.A.
MPO Box 707
Niagara Falls, NY 14302

In Canada
Harlequin Reader Service
Stratford, Ontario N5A 6W2

Please send me the following editions of The Warrender Saga.
I am enclosing my check or money order for $1.25 per novel
ordered, plus 49¢ to cover postage and handling.

☐   980 A Song Begins
☐ 1100 The Broken Wing
☐ 1244 When Love Is Blind
☐ 1405 The Curtain Rises
☐ 1508 Child of Music
☐ 1587 Music of the Heart
☐ 1767 Unbidden Melody
☐ 1834 Song Cycle

☐ 1936 Remembered Serenade

BONUS OFFER — *We Followed Our Stars*, Mary Burchell's
moving autobiography, is yours ABSOLUTELY FREE when
you purchase all nine Warrender Saga novels.
☐ Yes, I have purchased all nine of the above. Please send me
my copy of *We Followed Our Stars*.

Number of novels checked _____ @ $1.25 each = $ _____

We Followed Our Stars
Mary Burchell's autobiography _____ x $1.50 $ _____

Postage and handling $ _____.49

New York State and New Jersey residents please
add appropriate sales tax $ _____

                                    TOTAL $ _____

NAME _____
                        (Please Print)
ADDRESS _____

CITY _____

STATE/PROV _____ ZIP/POSTAL CODE _____

OFFER EXPIRES JUNE 30, 1979

A   ROM 2258

What readers say about Harlequin Romances

"Your books are the best I have ever found."
P.B.*, Bellevue, Washington

"I enjoy them more and more
with each passing year."
J.L., Spurlockville, West Virginia

"No matter how full and happy life might be,
it is an enchantment to sit
and read your novels."
D.K., Willowdale, Ontario

"I firmly believe that Harlequin Romances
are perfect for anyone who wants to read
a good romance."
C.R., Akron, Ohio

*Names available on request

And there's still *more* love in